Psalms and Ritual Music

Music for the Liturgy of the Word Year B

Revised

Complete Edition
WLP 003376

World Library Publications
the music and liturgy division of J. S. Paluch Company, Inc.
Franklin Park, Illinois

Psalms and Ritual Music

Music for the Liturgy of the Word
Year B
Revised

WLP 003376
Third Printing

ISBN 0-937690-95-3

Preface

Psalms and Ritual Music; Music for the Liturgy of the Word, Year A is one volume of a complete, easy-to-use resource for Lectionary psalmody, Gospel Acclamations, and various pieces of ritual music for the Church year. It is a helpful companion to the periodical and annual worship publications offered by World Library Publications, including *Seasonal Missalette®, We Celebrate Worship Resource®, ¡Celebremos!®, Word & Song,* and *Liturgy of the Word.*

The restoration of the Psalter to the Eucharistic Liturgy by Vatican Council II has borne some of the most abundant musical fruit of any of the liturgical reforms. As the late Joseph Cardinal Bernardin was fond of saying, when we chant the psalms' refrains, "we are learning the Church's most basic prayerbook." The chanting of the psalm verses to various tones is a centuries-old tradition in the Church.

The material in *Psalms and Ritual Music* is for the most part organized in the order of the Lectionary. For the psalms, a musical setting of the refrain precedes the verses underlaid to a psalm tone, and in a few instances, a through-composed musical setting of the verses is offered. Several musical settings for each season of Gospel Acclamations are offered. Following those are several more musical settings without verse text underlaid; these may be used as desired.

Pointing is the term describing the distribution of the words of the text to the notes of the psalm tone. Tones are in two halves; the first may contain an *intonation,* and always includes a *tenor* (or reciting pitch) and a *mediant* cadence; the second part includes a *tenor* and a *final* cadence. Most cadences include an optional note or slur to allow for a different number of syllables to be sung. The text in italic type shows syllables where the tenor or reciting pitch drops to a lower pitch, known as the *flex.* This inflection is used in very few psalms, and may be omitted.

Keyboard harmonizations for the Gregorian psalm tones were provided by Charles Thatcher. These revised harmonizations, grounded in the tradition of Gregorian chant practice, will enable a gracious musical support for the proclamation of the psalm verses. Charles Thatcher also underlaid the psalm verse texts to the Gregorian and modern chant tones. For further explanation of the principles employed in this process, lease see Notes on the pointing of the psalm verses on the following page.

This Revised Edition is offered to bring certain Psalms and Gospel Acclamations into agreement with the *Lectionary for Mass, Volumes II, III and IV,* which became mandatory for use in dioceses of the United States of America on Pentecost Sunday, May 19, 2002, and to correct errors in the first edition. Items that are revised from the first edition are identified by the word "Revised" beneath the number.

Notes on the pointing of the psalm verses

In the preparation of the pointed texts in *Psalms and Ritual Music* the need for some basic principles emerged; these were based upon liturgical context, linguistic factors and musical considerations.

Liturgical Context—The body of music we know today as psalm tones, especially the Gregorian tones, found their most extensive use in the chanting of the psalms for the Divine Office, most often by communities of religious men and women. The principles by which texts were pointed to these tones developed so that a group of people could chant together with consistency. In their current usage, the tones are utilized most often by a cantor or psalmist to proclaim the psalm during the Liturgy of the Word. A musical proclamation of the psalm text by an individual minister of the Word will generate different principles than simultaneous chanting of the same text by an entire community. The pointing of the psalm texts in *Psalms and Ritual Music* follows, as much as possible, a "proclamation rhythm." Some say that the chanting of a text should follow speech rhythm as closely as possible. Proclaiming the Word of God, however, is not precisely the same as speaking it. Therefore, the verse texts in this volume were pointed to enable their proclamation to the assembly. In cases where more than one way of pointing was possible, the psalm text was looked at in the context of the other proclamations of Scripture for that day, to ascertain if stressing the text one way or the other would help it resonate more clearly with the other passages from the Word of God.

Linguistic Factors—The movement from ecclesial Latin to vernacular English altered the basic rhythm of the psalm texts to a great degree. The musical principles which previously governed setting texts to the psalm tones emerged from their Latin usage, and so are not always useful for English. Aside from the basic difference in text and grammatical structure, English—like most languages of Anglo-Saxon or Teutonic origin—has a much more emphatic rhythm of inflection than Latin or other Romance languages. A stressed syllable in vernacular English will usually be more assertive than one in Latin. In English, a syllable misplaced at the flex, mediant, or final cadence of a psalm tone is a much more noticeable interruption of the "proclamation rhythm." Most often, the following will be found at the flex, mediant or cadence points of the tones in *Psalms and Ritual Music*:

- a change in grammatical unit (*i.e.,* a prepositional phrase or subordinate clause),

- internal punctuation (comma or semi-colon),

- an internal quotation, or

- a grammatically prominent word, especially a noun or verb.

Some tones are particularly challenging in English—tone 4, for example. This fact, however, does not warrant their exclusion, but demands even better preparation from those who chant them.

Musical Considerations—The psalm tones, at least the Gregorian tones, were intended to be chanted a cappella. In current pastoral praxis this is seldom the case. By providing these and other tones with musical accompaniment, they become part of the aural vocabulary of Western music, which attracts the ear to places of harmonic change. All the texts in *Psalms and Ritual Music* were pointed so they could be chanted a cappella. The texts were also pointed so that, when they are chanted with accompaniment, the emphasis will naturally occur at places of harmonic change, and so will not interrupt the rhythm of their proclamation. For those tones with longer cadence formulas, care was taken that final strong syllables were placed correctly. In a few instances two-note intonations are given to one-syllable words to avoid possible confusion as to the meaning of the text. No amount of careful pointing of these texts, however, will ever be a substitute for thoughtful and thorough preparation by the cantor or psalmist who takes the role of minister of the Word seriously.

The voice of the Holy Spirit in the psalms continues to sing to us in many, varied, beautiful and powerful ways. Pointing these texts—God's word in sung proclamation—might also be done in many, various ways, perhaps nearly as many as there are ministers of the word to proclaim them in song. Every time the psalms are proclaimed in the liturgy, it is the pastoral context and capabilities of the music ministers which will determine the final form they take. The pointing of every text herein was done out of a sincere desire to assist pastoral musicians in proclaiming these texts, in hopes that the proclamation of the Responsorial Psalm might fulfill the greater goal of the Liturgy of the Word as envisioned by Vatican II: "to open up the treasures of Scripture more lavishly."

Alan J. Hommerding

First Sunday of Advent   B1
Psalm 80:2–3, 15–16, 18–19

RESPONSE: *Psalm 80:4*

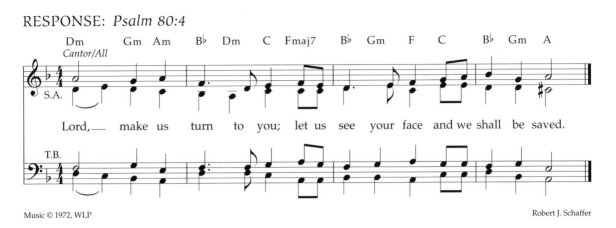

Lord,— make us turn to you; let us see your face and we shall be saved.

Music © 1972, WLP

Robert J. Schaffer

VERSES

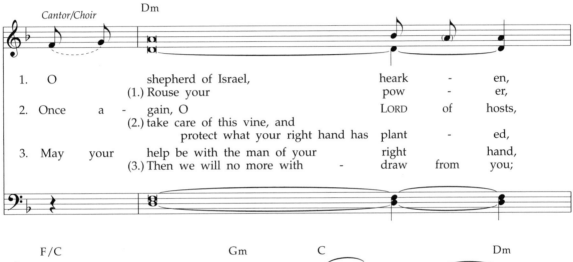

1. O shepherd of Israel, heark - en,
(1.) Rouse your pow - er,
2. Once a - gain, O LORD of hosts,
(2.) take care of this vine, and protect what your right hand has plant - ed,
3. May your help be with the man of your right hand,
(3.) Then we will no more with - draw from you;

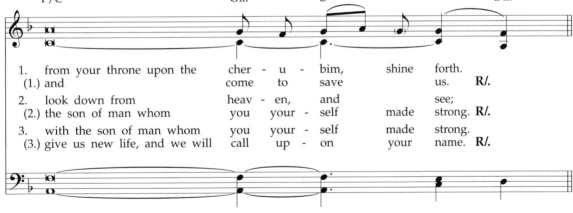

1. from your throne upon the cher - u - bim, shine forth.
(1.) and come to save us. **R/.**
2. look down from heav - en, and see;
(2.) the son of man whom you your - self made strong. **R/.**
3. with the son of man whom you your - self made strong.
(3.) give us new life, and we will call up - on your name. **R/.**

Music © 2000, WLP

Tone 1f, adapt.

B2   Second Sunday of Advent
Psalm 85:9–10, 11–12, 13–14

RESPONSE: *Psalm 85:8*

Lord, let us see your kind-ness, and grant us your sal - va - tion.

Am   G   Am   Am/C Dm7 Em   F   Em6 Am sus   Am

Music © 1999, WLP

Paul M. French

VERSES

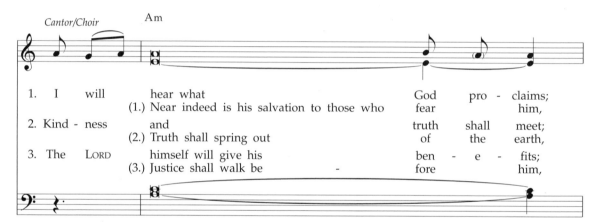

Cantor/Choir   Am

1. I will hear what God pro - claims;
(1.) Near indeed is his salvation to those who fear him,
2. Kind - ness and truth shall meet;
(2.) Truth shall spring out of the earth,
3. The LORD himself will give his ben - e - fits;
(3.) Justice shall walk be - fore him,

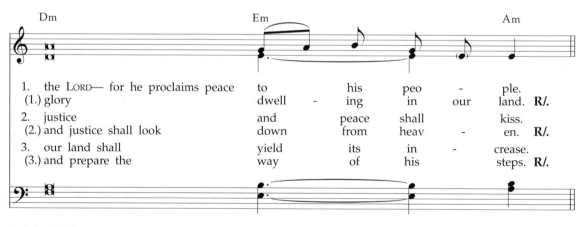

Dm   Em   Am

1. the LORD— for he proclaims peace to his peo - ple.
(1.) glory dwell - ing in our land. **R/.**
2. justice and peace shall kiss.
(2.) and justice shall look down from heav - en. **R/.**
3. our land shall yield its in - crease.
(3.) and prepare the way of his steps. **R/.**

Music © 2000, WLP

Tone 4A, adapt.

Third Sunday of Advent B3
Luke 1:46–48, 49–50, 53–54

RESPONSE: *Isaiah 61:10*

Music © 1989, WLP

Anthony J. Greening, 1940–1996

VERSES

1. My soul proclaims the greatness of the Lord;
(1.) for he has looked upon his lowly serv - ant.
2. The Al - mighty has done great things for me,
(2.) He has mercy on those who fear him
3. He has filled the hungry with good things,
(3.) He has come to the help of his servant Is - ra - el

1. my spirit rejoices in God my Sav - ior,
(1.) From this day all generations will call me bless - ed: **R/.**
2. and ho - ly is his Name.
(2.) in every gen - er - a - tion. **R/.**
3. and the rich he has sent a - way emp - ty.
(3.) for he has remembered his prom - ise of mer - cy. **R/.**

Music © 2000, WLP

Tone 8G

RESPONSE: *Psalm 89:2a*

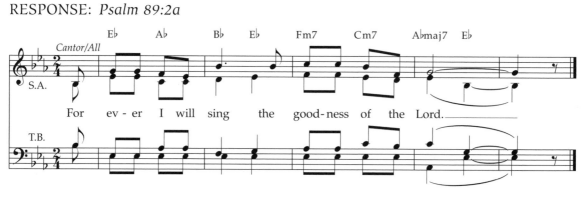

Forever I will sing the goodness of the Lord.

Music © 1984, WLP

Robert E. Kreutz, 1922–1996

VERSES

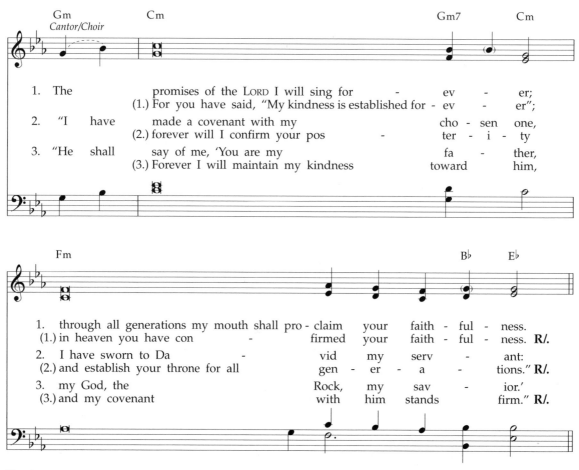

1. The promises of the LORD I will sing for - ev - er;
(1.) For you have said, "My kindness is established for - ev - er";
2. "I have made a covenant with my cho - sen one,
(2.) forever will I confirm your pos - ter - i - ty
3. "He shall say of me, 'You are my fa - ther,
(3.) Forever I will maintain my kindness toward him,

1. through all generations my mouth shall pro - claim your faith - ful - ness.
(1.) in heaven you have con - firmed your faith - ful - ness. **R/.**
2. I have sworn to Da - vid my serv - ant:
(2.) and establish your throne for all gen - er - a - tions." **R/.**
3. my God, the Rock, my sav - ior.'
(3.) and my covenant with him stands firm." **R/.**

Music © 1982, WLP

Robert E. Kreutz, 1922–1996

Christmas, at the Vigil Mass   B5
Psalm 89:4–5, 16–17, 27, 29

RESPONSE: *Psalm 89:2a*

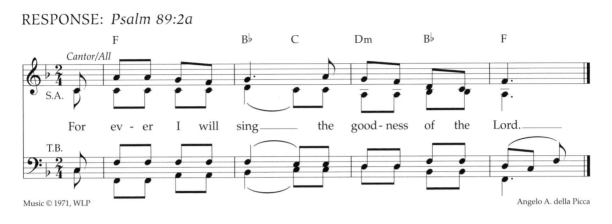

For ev - er I will sing___ the good - ness of the Lord.___

Music © 1971, WLP

Angelo A. della Picca

VERSES

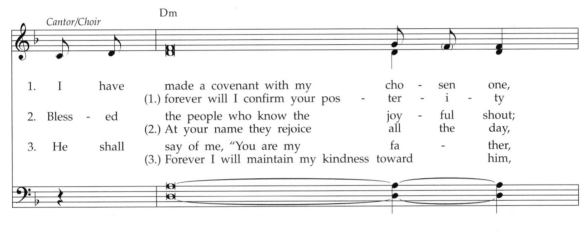

1. I have made a covenant with my cho - sen one,
(1.) forever will I confirm your pos - ter - i - ty
2. Bless - ed the people who know the joy - ful shout;
(2.) At your name they rejoice all the day,
3. He shall say of me, "You are my fa - ther,
(3.) Forever I will maintain my kindness toward him,

1. I have sworn to Da - vid my serv - ant:
(1.) and establish your throne for all gen - er - a - tions. **R/.**
2. in the light of your counte - nance, O LORD, they walk.
(2.) and through your justice they are ex - alt - ed. **R/.**
3. my God, the rock, my sav - ior."
(3.) and my covenant with him stands firm. **R/.**

Music © 2000, WLP

Tone 3g, adapt.

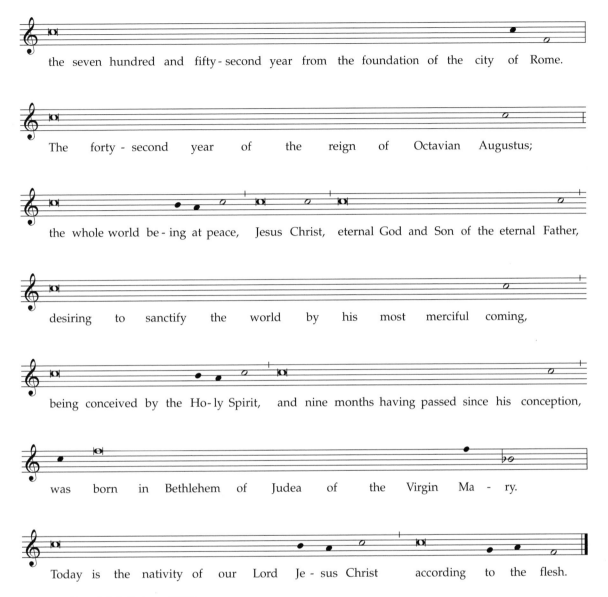

the seven hundred and fifty - second year from the foundation of the city of Rome.

The forty - second year of the reign of Octavian Augustus;

the whole world be - ing at peace, Jesus Christ, eternal God and Son of the eternal Father,

desiring to sanctify the world by his most merciful coming,

being conceived by the Ho - ly Spirit, and nine months having passed since his conception,

was born in Bethlehem of Judea of the Virgin Ma - ry.

Today is the nativity of our Lord Je - sus Christ according to the flesh.

B7 Christmas, Mass at Midnight
Psalm 96:1–2, 2–3, 11–12, 13

RESPONSE: *Luke 2:11*

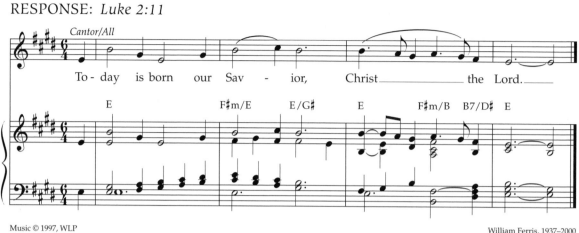

Today is born our Savior, Christ the Lord.

Music © 1997, WLP

William Ferris, 1937–2000

VERSES

1. Sing to the LORD a new *song;* sing to the LORD, all you lands.
2. Announce his salvation, day after *day.* Tell his glory among the na - tions;
3. Let the heavens be glad and the earth re - joice;
   (3.) let the plains be joyful and all that is in them!
4. They shall exult before the LORD, for he comes;
   (4.) He shall rule the world with jus - tice

1. Sing to the LORD; bless his name. **R/.**
2. among all peoples, his won - drous deeds. **R/.**
3. let the sea and what fills it re - sound;
   (3.) Then shall all the trees of the for - est ex - ult. **R/.**
4. for he comes to rule the earth.
   (4.) and the peoples with his con - stan - cy. **R/.**

Music © 1981, WLP

Tone 1f, adapt.

Christmas, Mass at Dawn   B8
Psalm 97:1, 6, 11–12

RESPONSE

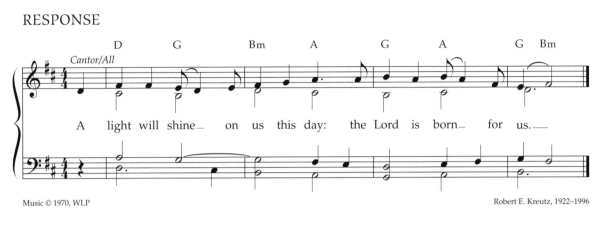

A light will shine— on us this day: the Lord is born— for us.—

Robert E. Kreutz, 1922–1996

VERSES

1. The LORD is king; let the earth re - joice;
(1.) The heavens proclaim his jus - tice,
2. Light dawns for the just;
(2.) Be glad in the LORD, you just,

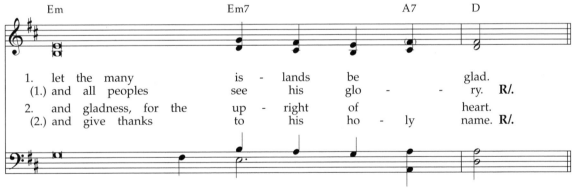

1. let the many is - lands be glad.
(1.) and all peoples see his glo - - ry. **R/.**
2. and gladness, for the up - right of heart.
(2.) and give thanks to his ho - ly name. **R/.**

Robert E. Kreutz, 1922–1996

RESPONSE: *Psalm 98:3c*

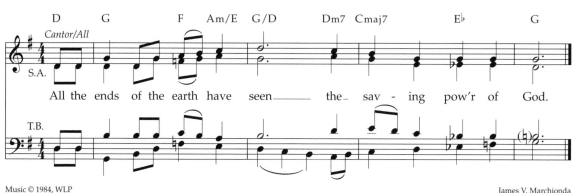

Music © 1984, WLP   James V. Marchionda

VERSES

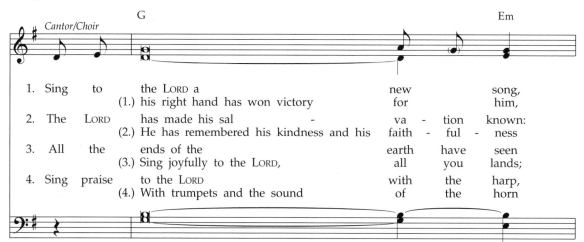

1. Sing   to   the Lord a   new   song,
   (1.) his right hand has won victory   for   him,
2. The   Lord   has made his sal   -   va - tion   known:
   (2.) He has remembered his kindness and his faith - ful - ness
3. All   the   ends of the   earth   have   seen
   (3.) Sing joyfully to the Lord,   all   you   lands;
4. Sing praise   to the Lord   with   the   harp,
   (4.) With trumpets and the sound   of   the   horn

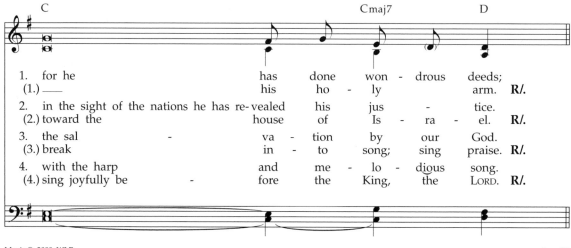

1. for he   has   done   won - drous   deeds;
   (1.) ——   his   ho - ly   arm. **R/.**
2. in the sight of the nations he has re- vealed his   jus - tice.
   (2.) toward the   house of   Is - ra - el. **R/.**
3. the sal   -   va - tion   by   our   God.
   (3.) break   in - to   song; sing   praise. **R/.**
4. with the harp   and   me - lo - dious   song.
   (4.) sing joyfully be - fore the   King,   the   Lord. **R/.**

Music © 2000, WLP   Tone 8G

The Holy Family   B10
Psalm 128:1–2, 3, 4–5

This psalm may be used in Years A, B, and C.

RESPONSE: *cf. Psalm 128:1*

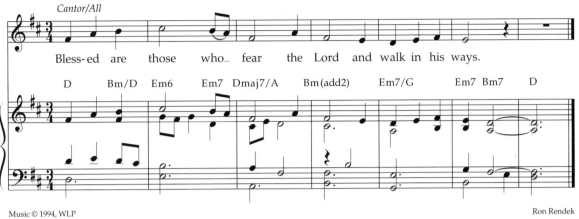

Music © 1994, WLP   Ron Rendek

VERSES

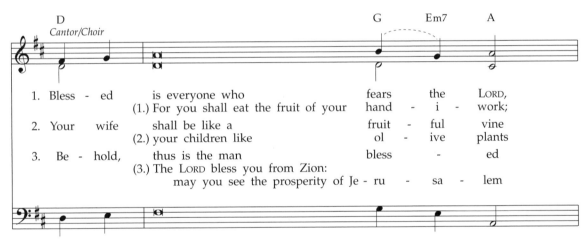

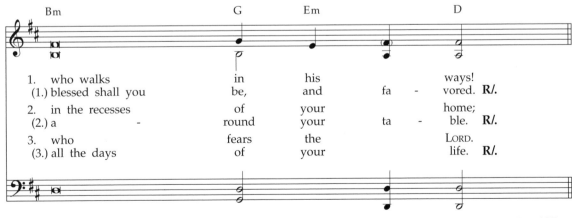

Music © 1984, WLP   James M. Burns

B11 The Holy Family
Psalm 105:1–2, 3–4, 5–6, 8–9

This psalm may be used in Year B.

RESPONSE: *Psalm 105:7a, 8a*

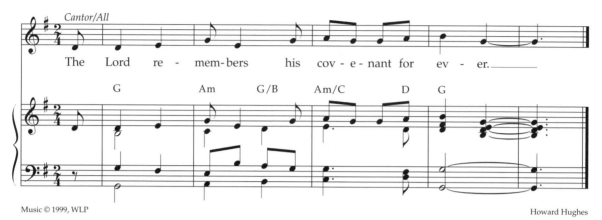

The Lord re-mem-bers his cov-e-nant for ev-er.

Music © 1999, WLP

Howard Hughes

VERSES

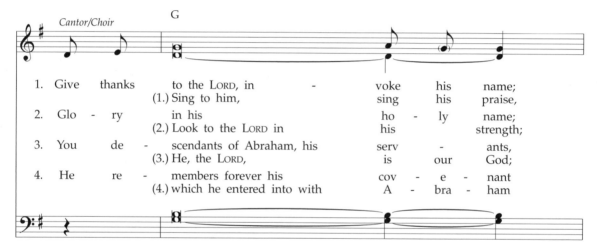

1. Give thanks to the LORD, in-voke his name;
(1.) Sing to him, sing his praise,

2. Glo-ry in his ho-ly name;
(2.) Look to the LORD in his strength;

3. You de-scendants of Abraham, his serv-ants,
(3.) He, the LORD, is our God;

4. He re-members forever his cov-e-nant
(4.) which he entered into with A-bra-ham

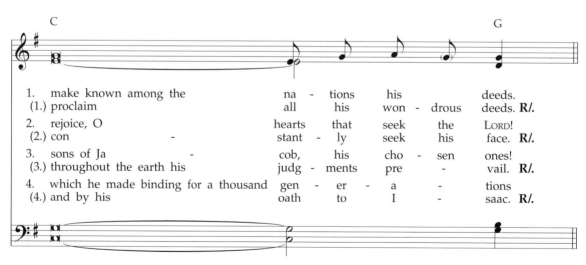

1. make known among the na-tions his deeds.
(1.) proclaim all his won-drous deeds. **R/.**

2. rejoice, O hearts that seek the LORD!
(2.) con-stant-ly seek his face. **R/.**

3. sons of Ja-cob, his cho-sen ones!
(3.) throughout the earth his judg-ments pre-vail. **R/.**

4. which he made binding for a thousand gen-er-a-tions
(4.) and by his oath to I-saac. **R/.**

Music © 2000, WLP

Tone 8c

Mary, the Mother of God B12
Psalm 67:2–3, 5, 6, 8

RESPONSE: *Psalm 67:2a*

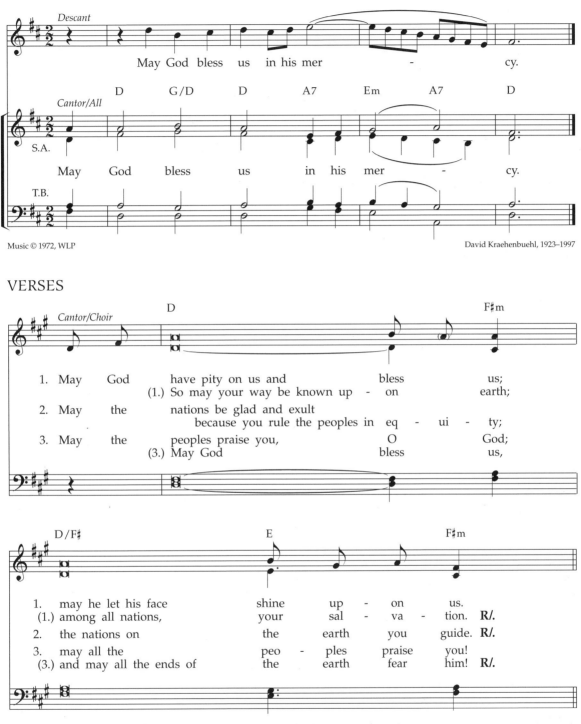

Music © 1972, WLP   David Kraehenbuehl, 1923–1997

VERSES

1. May God have pity on us and bless us;
(1.) So may your way be known up - on earth;
2. May the nations be glad and exult
because you rule the peoples in eq - ui - ty;
3. May the peoples praise you, O God;
(3.) May God bless us,

1. may he let his face shine up - on us.
(1.) among all nations, your sal - va - tion. **R/.**
2. the nations on the earth you guide. **R/.**
3. may all the peo - ples praise you!
(3.) and may all the ends of the earth fear him! **R/.**

Music © 2000, WLP   Tone 5

B13 Second Sunday after Christmas
Psalm 147:12–13, 14–15, 19–20

RESPONSE: *John 1:14*

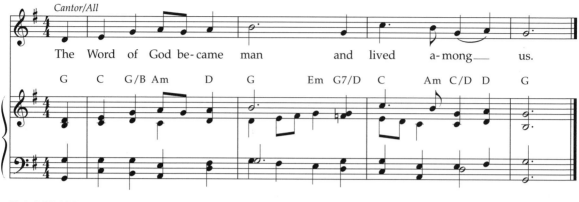

The Word of God be-came man and lived a-mong us.

Music © 1999, WLP   Thomas Strickland

A sung Alleluia *may replace this response.*

VERSES

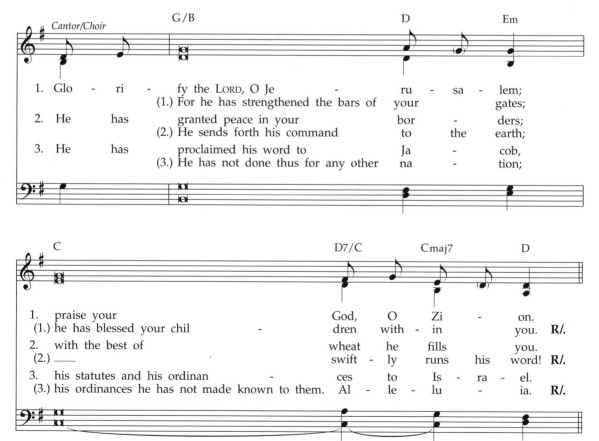

1. Glo - ri - fy the LORD, O Je - ru - sa - lem;
(1.) For he has strengthened the bars of your gates;
2. He has granted peace in your bor - ders;
(2.) He sends forth his command to the earth;
3. He has proclaimed his word to Ja - cob,
(3.) He has not done thus for any other na - tion;

1. praise your God, O Zi - on.
(1.) he has blessed your chil - dren with - in you. **R/.**
2. with the best of wheat he fills you.
(2.) —— swift - ly runs his word! **R/.**
3. his statutes and his ordinan - ces to Is - ra - el.
(3.) his ordinances he has not made known to them. Al - le - lu - ia. **R/.**

Music © 1972, WLP   Tone 8G

The Epiphany of the Lord   B14
Psalm 72:1-2, 7-8, 10–11, 12–13

RESPONSE: *cf. Psalm 72:11*

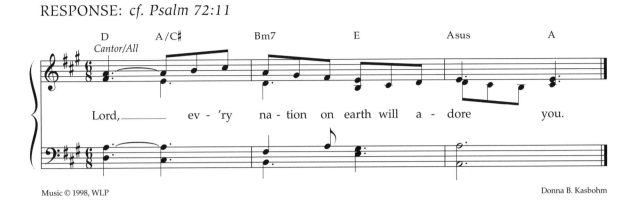

Lord, ev - 'ry nation on earth will a - dore you.

Music © 1998, WLP

Donna B. Kasbohm

VERSES

Cantor/Choir

1. O God, with your judgment en - dow the king,
(1.) he shall govern your people with jus - tice

2. Jus - tice shall flower in his days,
(2.) May he rule from sea to sea,

3. The kings of Tarshish and the Isles shall of - fer gifts;
(3.) All kings shall pay him hom - age,

4. For he shall rescue the poor when he cries out,
(4.) He shall have pity for the lowly and the poor;

1. and with your jus - tice, the king's son;
(1.) and your afflicted ones with judg - ment. **R/.**

2. and profound peace, till the moon be no more.
(2.) and from the River to the ends of the earth. **R/.**

3. the kings of Arabia and Seba shall bring trib - ute.
(3.) all na - tions shall serve him. **R/.**

4. and the afflicted when he has no one to help him.
(4.) the lives of the poor he shall save. **R/.**

Music © 2000, WLP

Tone 8c

The Baptism of the Lord
Psalm 29:1–2, 3–4, 3, 9–10

This psalm may be used in Years A, B, and C.

RESPONSE: *Psalm 29:11b*

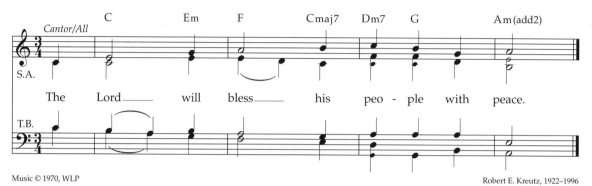

The Lord will bless his peo-ple with peace.

Music © 1970, WLP

Robert E. Kreutz, 1922–1996

VERSES

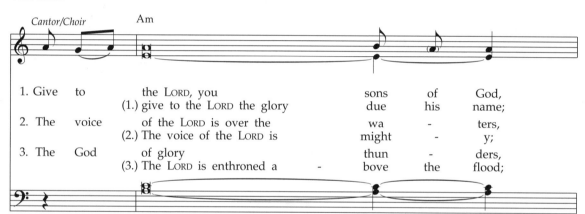

1. Give to the LORD, you sons of God,
(1.) give to the LORD the glory due his name;
2. The voice of the LORD is over the wa - ters,
(2.) The voice of the LORD is might - y;
3. The God of glory thun - ders,
(3.) The LORD is enthroned a - bove the flood;

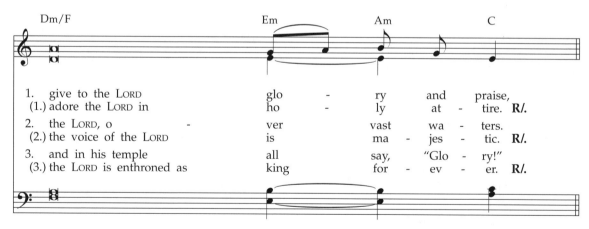

1. give to the LORD glo - ry and praise,
(1.) adore the LORD in ho - ly at - tire. **R/.**
2. the LORD, o - ver vast wa - ters.
(2.) the voice of the LORD is ma - jes - tic. **R/.**
3. and in his temple all say, "Glo - ry!"
(3.) the LORD is enthroned as king for - ev - er. **R/.**

Music © 2000, WLP

Tone 4A, adapt.

The Baptism of the Lord   B16
Isaiah 12:2–3, 4bcd, 5–6

This psalm may be used in Year B.

RESPONSE: *Isaiah 12:3*

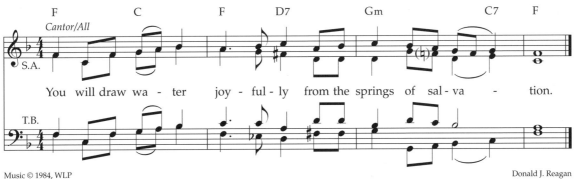

You will draw wa-ter joy-ful-ly from the springs of sal-va-tion.

Music © 1984, WLP   Donald J. Reagan

VERSES

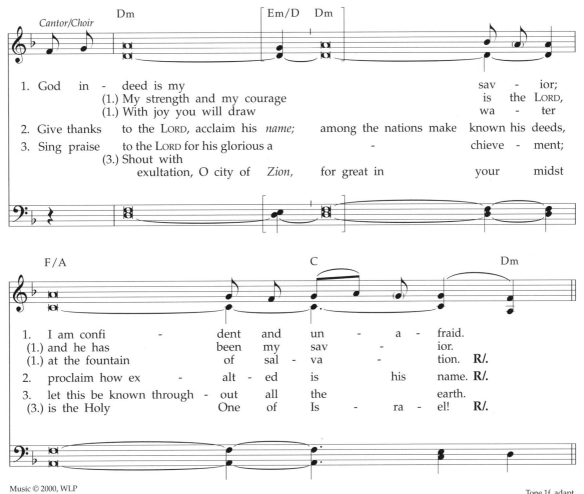

1. God in - deed is my   sav - ior;
   (1.) My strength and my courage   is   the LORD,
   (1.) With joy you will draw   wa - ter
2. Give thanks   to the LORD, acclaim his *name*;   among the nations make   known his deeds,
3. Sing praise   to the LORD for his glorious a   -   chieve - ment;
   (3.) Shout with
        exultation, O city of *Zion*,   for great in   your   midst

1. I am confi   -   dent and un - a - fraid.
   (1.) and he has   been   my   sav   -   ior.
   (1.) at the fountain   of   sal - va   -   tion. **R/.**
2. proclaim how ex - alt - ed   is   his   name. **R/.**
3. let this be known through - out   all   the   earth.
   (3.) is the Holy   One   of   Is - ra - el! **R/.**

Music © 2000, WLP   Tone 1f, adapt.

B17 Ash Wednesday
Psalm 51:3–4, 5–6ab, 12–13, 14, 17

RESPONSE: *Psalm 51:3*

Michael Bedford

VERSES

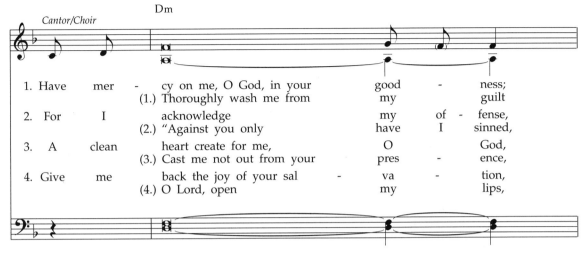

1. Have mer - cy on me, O God, in your good - ness;
   (1.) Thoroughly wash me from my guilt
2. For I acknowledge my of - fense,
   (2.) "Against you only have I sinned,
3. A clean heart create for me, O God,
   (3.) Cast me not out from your pres - ence,
4. Give me back the joy of your sal - va - tion,
   (4.) O Lord, open my lips,

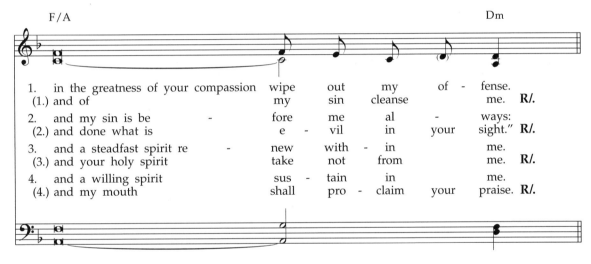

1. in the greatness of your compassion wipe out my of - fense.
   (1.) and of my sin cleanse me. **R/.**
2. and my sin is be - fore me al - ways:
   (2.) and done what is e - vil in your sight." **R/.**
3. and a steadfast spirit re - new with - in me.
   (3.) and your holy spirit take not from me. **R/.**
4. and a willing spirit sus - tain in me.
   (4.) and my mouth shall pro - claim your praise. **R/.**

Music © 2000, WLP

Tone 2

B18 First Sunday of Lent
Psalm 25:4–5, 6–7, 8–9

RESPONSE: *cf. Psalm 25:10*

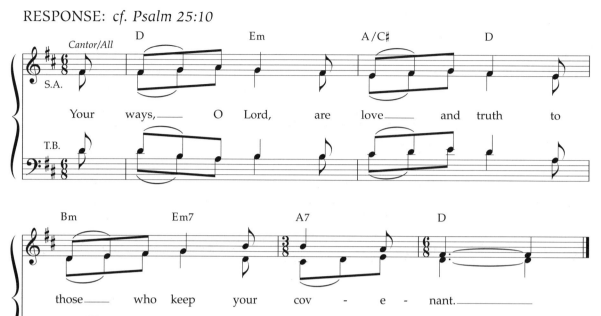

Your ways,___ O Lord, are love___ and truth to those___ who keep your cov - e - nant.___

Robert E. Kreutz, 1922–1996

VERSES

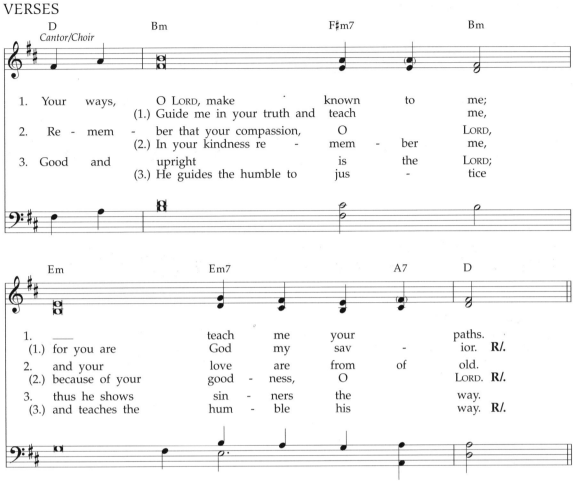

1. Your ways, O Lord, make known to me;
   (1.) Guide me in your truth and teach me,
2. Re - mem - ber that your compassion, O Lord,
   (2.) In your kindness re - mem - ber me,
3. Good and upright is the Lord;
   (3.) He guides the humble to jus - tice

1. _____ teach me your paths.
   (1.) for you are God my sav - ior. **R/.**
2. and your love are from of old.
   (2.) because of your good - ness, O Lord. **R/.**
3. thus he shows sin - ners the way.
   (3.) and teaches the hum - ble his way. **R/.**

Robert E. Kreutz, 1922–1996

B19 Second Sunday of Lent
Psalm 116:10, 15–19

RESPONSE: *Psalm 116:9*

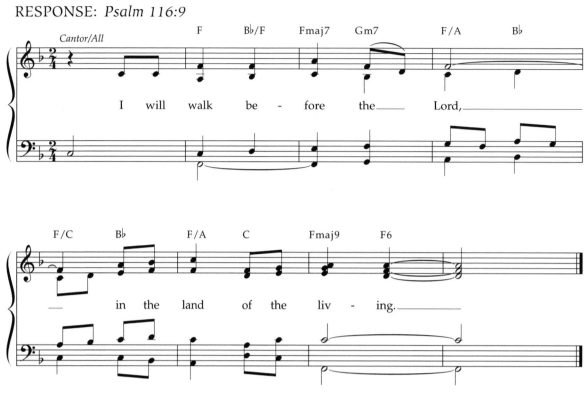

I will walk be - fore the Lord, in the land of the liv - ing.

Music © 1994, WLP

Howard Hughes

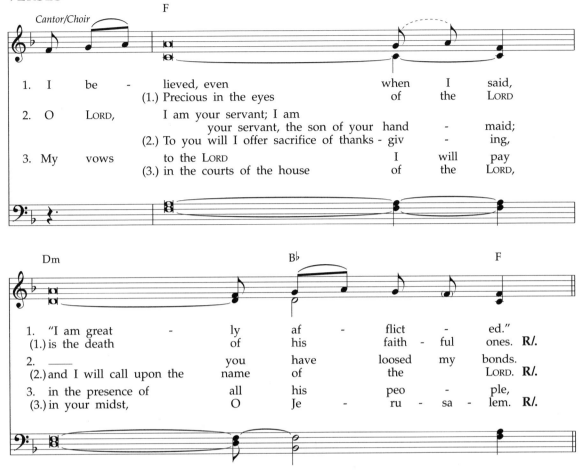

Music © 2000, WLP

Tone 6

B20 Third Sunday of Lent
Psalm 19:8, 9, 10, 11

RESPONSE: *John 6:68c*

Marty Haugen

VERSES

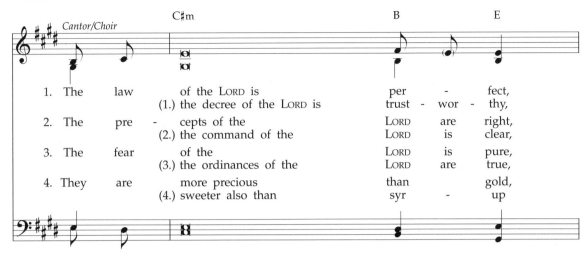

1. The law of the LORD is per - fect,
   (1.) the decree of the LORD is trust - wor - thy,
2. The pre - cepts of the LORD are right,
   (2.) the command of the LORD is clear,
3. The fear of the LORD is pure,
   (3.) the ordinances of the LORD are true,
4. They are more precious than gold,
   (4.) sweeter also than syr - up

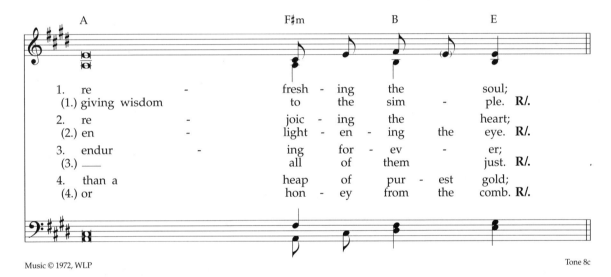

1. re - fresh - ing the soul;
   (1.) giving wisdom to the sim - ple. **R/.**
2. re - joic - ing the heart;
   (2.) en - light - en - ing the eye. **R/.**
3. endur - ing for - ev - er;
   (3.) —— all of them just. **R/.**
4. than a heap of pur - est gold;
   (4.) or hon - ey from the comb. **R/.**

Tone 8c

B21 Third Sunday of Lent — Year A
Psalm 95:1–2, 6–7, 8–9

This psalm is used for the First Scrutiny of the Elect.

RESPONSE: *Psalm 95:8*

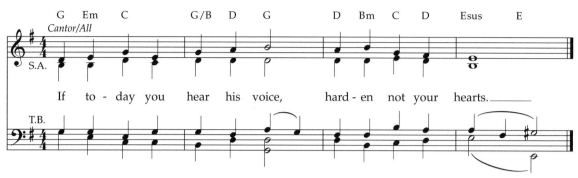

If to-day you hear his voice, hard-en not your hearts.

Music © 1984, WLP

David N. Johnson, 1922–1987

VERSES

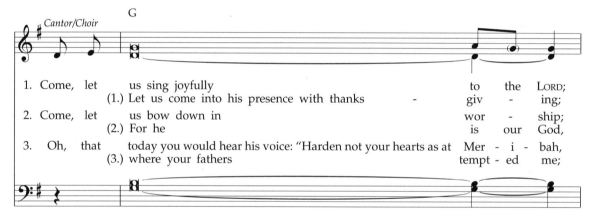

1. Come, let us sing joyfully to the LORD;
(1.) Let us come into his presence with thanks - giv - ing;
2. Come, let us bow down in wor - ship;
(2.) For he is our God,
3. Oh, that today you would hear his voice: "Harden not your hearts as at Mer - i - bah,
(3.) where your fathers tempt - ed me;

1. let us acclaim the Rock of our sal - va - tion.
(1.) let us joyful - ly sing psalms to him. **R/.**
2. let us kneel before the LORD who made us.
(2.) and we are the people he shepherds, the flock he guides. **R/.**
3. as in the day of Massah in the des - ert,
(3.) they tested me though they had seen my works." **R/.**

Music © 2000, WLP

Tone 8c

Fourth Sunday of Lent   B22
Psalm 137:1–2, 3, 4–5, 6

RESPONSE: *Psalm 137:6ab*

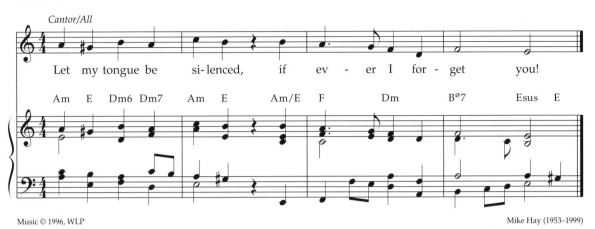

Let my tongue be si-lenced, if ev-er I for-get you!

Music © 1996, WLP

Mike Hay (1953–1999)

VERSES

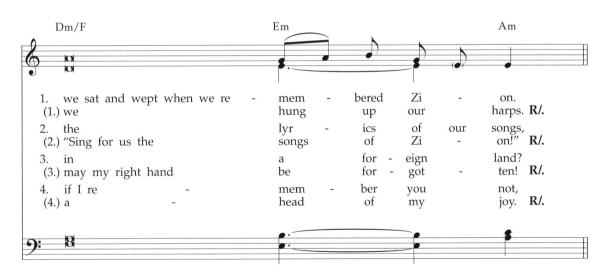

1. By the streams of Bab - y - lon
(1.) On the aspens of that land

2. For there our captors asked of us
(2.) and our despoilers urged us to be joy - ous:

3. How could we sing a song of the LORD
(3.) If I forget you, Je - ru - sa - lem,

4. May my tongue cleave to my pal - ate
(4.) if I place not Je - ru - sa - lem

1. we sat and wept when we re - mem - bered Zi - on.
(1.) we hung up our harps. **R/.**

2. the lyr - ics of our songs,
(2.) "Sing for us the songs of Zi - on!" **R/.**

3. in a for - eign land?
(3.) may my right hand be for - got - ten! **R/.**

4. if I re - mem - ber you not,
(4.) a - head of my joy. **R/.**

Music © 2000, WLP

Tone 4A, adapt.

B23 Fourth Sunday of Lent — Year A
Psalm 23:1–3a, 3b-4, 5, 6

This psalm is used for the Second Scrutiny of the Elect.

RESPONSE: *Psalm 23:1*

The Lord is my shep - herd; there is noth - ing I shall want.

Music © 1970, WLP   Angelo A. della Picca

VERSES

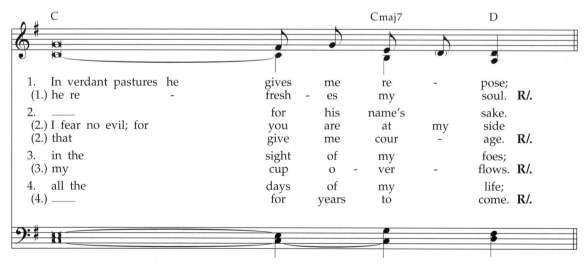

1.	The Lord	is my shepherd; I		shall	not	want.
	(1.) beside restful waters he			leads		me;
2.	He guides	me in		right		paths
	(2.) Even though I walk in the dark			val	-	ley
	(2.) with your rod and			your		staff
3.	You spread	the table be	-	fore		me
	(3.) you anoint my			head	with	oil;
4.	On - ly	goodness and kindness		fol	- low	me
	(4.) and I shall dwell in the house			of	the	Lord

1.	In verdant pastures he	gives	me	re -	pose;
	(1.) he re -	fresh - es	my		soul. R/.
2.	___	for	his	name's	sake.
	(2.) I fear no evil; for	you	are	at my	side
	(2.) that	give	me	cour -	age. R/.
3.	in the	sight	of	my	foes;
	(3.) my	cup	o - ver -		flows. R/.
4.	all the	days	of	my	life;
	(4.) ___	for	years	to	come. R/.

Music © 2000, WLP   Tone 8G

Fifth Sunday of Lent   B24
Psalm 51:3–4, 12–13, 14–15

RESPONSE: *Psalm 51:12a*

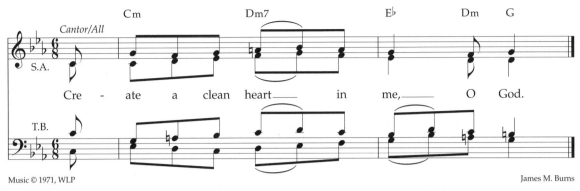

Cre - ate a clean heart____ in me,____ O God.

Music © 1971, WLP   James M. Burns

VERSES

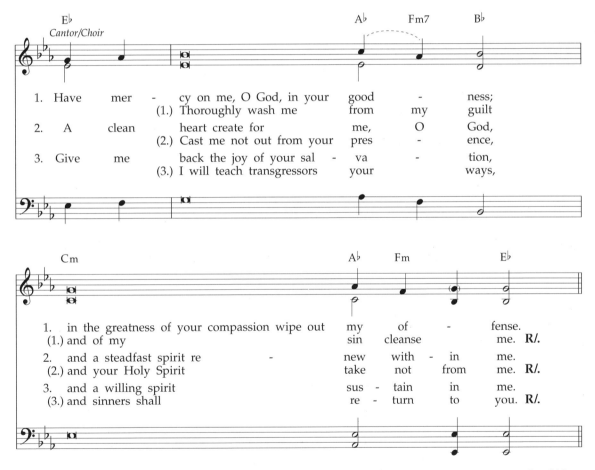

1. Have mer - cy on me, O God, in your good - ness;
(1.) Thoroughly wash me from my guilt
2. A clean heart create for me, O God,
(2.) Cast me not out from your pres - ence,
3. Give me back the joy of your sal - va - tion,
(3.) I will teach transgressors your ways,

1. in the greatness of your compassion wipe out my of - fense.
(1.) and of my sin cleanse me. **R/.**
2. and a steadfast spirit re - new with - in me.
(2.) and your Holy Spirit take not from me. **R/.**
3. and a willing spirit sus - tain in me.
(3.) and sinners shall re - turn to you. **R/.**

Music © 1981, WLP   James M. Burns

B25   Fifth Sunday of Lent — Year A
Psalm 130:1–2, 3–4, 5–7, 7–8

This psalm is used for the Third Scrutiny of the Elect.

RESPONSE: *Psalm 130:7*

Music © 1999, WLP

Michael Bogdan

VERSES

1. Out of the depths I cry to you, O LORD;
   (1.) Let your ears be at - ten - tive
2. If you, O LORD, mark in - iq - ui - ties,
   (2.) But with you is for - give - ness,
3. I trust in the LORD;
   (3.) More than sentinels wait for the dawn,
4. For with the LORD is kind - ness
   (4.) and he will redeem Is - ra - el

1. _____ LORD, hear my voice!
   (1.) to my voice in sup - pli - ca - tion. **R/.**
2. _____ LORD, who can stand?
   (2.) that you may be re - vered. **R/.**
3. my soul trusts in his word.
   (3.) let Israel wait for the LORD. **R/.**
4. and with him is plen - teous re - demp - tion;
   (4.) from all their in - iq - ui - ties. **R/.**

Music © 1984, WLP

Donald J. Reagan

Palm Sunday of the Lord's Passion, B26
at the Procession with Palms
Opening Antiphon

RESPONSE: *Matthew 21:9*

INTRODUCTION

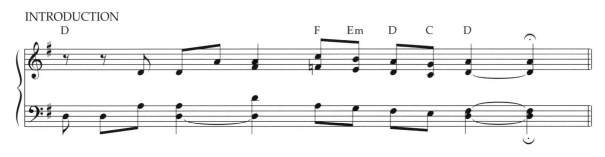

Ho - san - na to the Son of Da - vid, the King of

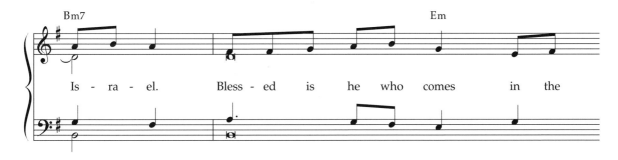

Is - ra - el. Bless - ed is he who comes in the

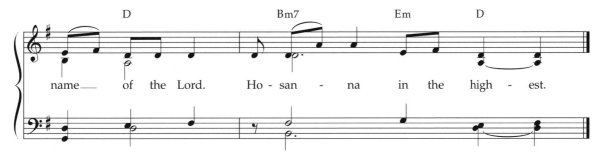

name___ of the Lord. Ho - san - na in the high - est.

Adapted from the chant by Nicholas T. Freund
Acc. by Theophane Hytrek, 1915–1992

B27 Palm Sunday of the Lord's Passion, at the Procession with Palms
Psalm 24:1-10

RESPONSE: *Matthew 21:8-9*

INTRODUCTION

The chil-dren of Je-ru-sa-lem wel-comed Christ the King. They car-ried ol-ive branch-es and loud-ly praised the Lord: Ho-san-na in the high-est.

Music © 1982, WLP

Adapted from the chant by Nicholas T. Freund
Acc. by Theophane Hytrek, 1915–1992

VERSES

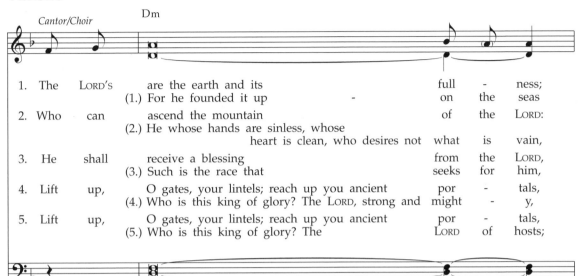

1. The LORD'S are the earth and its full - ness;
(1.) For he founded it up - on the seas
2. Who can ascend the mountain of the LORD:
(2.) He whose hands are sinless, whose
heart is clean, who desires not what is vain,
3. He shall receive a blessing from the LORD,
(3.) Such is the race that seeks for him,
4. Lift up, O gates, your lintels; reach up you ancient por - tals,
(4.) Who is this king of glory? The LORD, strong and might - y,
5. Lift up, O gates, your lintels; reach up you ancient por - tals,
(5.) Who is this king of glory? The LORD of hosts;

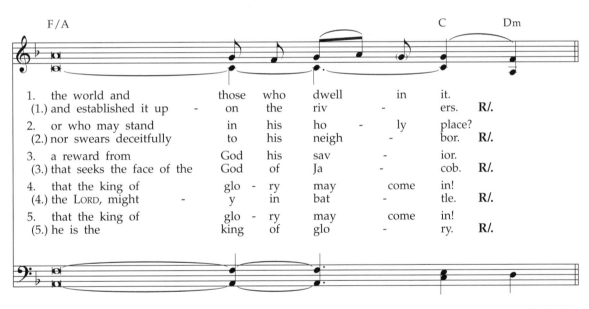

1. the world and those who dwell in it.
(1.) and established it up - on the riv - ers. **R/.**
2. or who may stand in his ho - ly place?
(2.) nor swears deceitfully to his neigh - bor. **R/.**
3. a reward from God his sav - ior.
(3.) that seeks the face of the God of Ja - cob. **R/.**
4. that the king of glo - ry may come in!
(4.) the LORD, might - y in bat - tle. **R/.**
5. that the king of glo - ry may come in!
(5.) he is the king of glo - ry. **R/.**

Tone 1f, adapt.

**B28 Palm Sunday of the Lord's Passion,
at the Procession with Palms
Psalm 47:2-10**

RESPONSE: *Mark 11:8-10*

Adapted from the chant by Nicholas T. Freund
Acc. by Theophane Hytrek, 1915–1992

VERSES

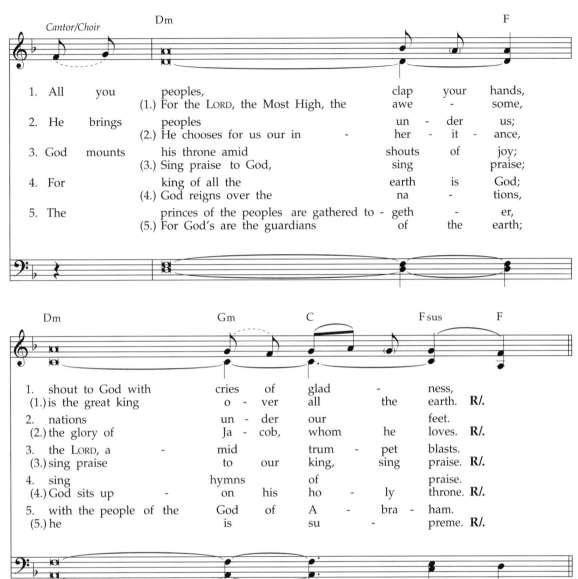

1. All you peoples, clap your hands,
(1.) For the LORD, the Most High, the awe - some,

2. He brings peoples un - der us;
(2.) He chooses for us our in - her - it - ance,

3. God mounts his throne amid shouts of joy;
(3.) Sing praise to God, sing praise;

4. For king of all the earth is God;
(4.) God reigns over the na - tions,

5. The princes of the peoples are gathered to - geth - er,
(5.) For God's are the guardians of the earth;

1. shout to God with cries of glad - ness,
(1.) is the great king o - ver all the earth. **R/.**

2. nations un - der our feet.
(2.) the glory of Ja - cob, whom he loves. **R/.**

3. the LORD, a - mid trum - pet blasts.
(3.) sing praise to our king, sing praise. **R/.**

4. sing hymns of praise.
(4.) God sits up - on his ho - ly throne. **R/.**

5. with the people of the God of A - bra - ham.
(5.) he is su - preme. **R/.**

Tone 1f, adapt.

B29 Palm Sunday of the Lord's Passion, at the Mass
Psalm 22:2, 8–9, 17–18, 19–20, 23–24

LECT. 38

RESPONSE: *Psalm 22:2a*

My God,— my God,— why have you a-ban-doned me?—

Music © 1995, WLP

Richard T. Proulx

VERSES *

1. — All who— see me scoff at me;— — they
2. In-deed, man-y dogs sur-round— me,— — a
3. — They di-vide my gar-ments a-mong them,
4. — I will pro-claim your name— to my breth-ren;

1. mock— me with part-ed— lips,— they wag their— heads:—
2. pack of e-vil do-ers— clos-es in up-on me;
3. — and for my ves-ture — they cast lots.—
4. — in the midst of the as-sem-bly — I will praise you.

*Verses set to a psalm tone follow.

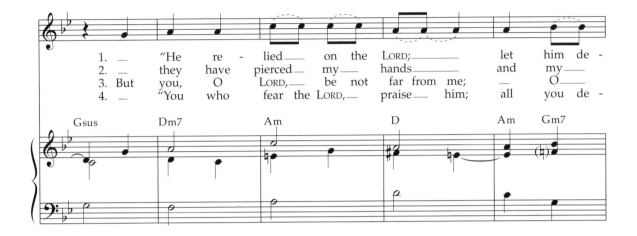

1. — "He re - lied— on the LORD; — let him de -
2. — they have pierced— my— hands— and my
3. But you, O LORD,— be not far from me; — O —
4. — "You who fear the LORD,— praise— him; all you de -

Gsus   Dm7   Am   D   Am   Gm7

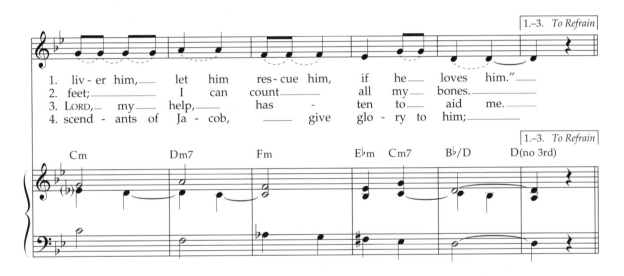

1.–3. *To Refrain*

1. liv- er him,— let him res - cue him, if he loves him."
2. feet; I can count— all my bones.
3. LORD,— my— help, has - ten to aid me.
4. scend - ants of Ja - cob, — give glo - ry to him; —

1.–3. *To Refrain*

Cm   Dm7   Fm   E♭m Cm7   B♭/D   D(no 3rd)

4.   *To Refrain*

4. — re - vere him, all you de - scend - ants of Is - rael." —

4.

D(no 3rd)   Dm7   Fm   E♭m Cm7   B♭/D   D(no 3rd)   *To Refrain*

Richard T. Proulx

RESPONSE: *Psalm 22:2*

My God,— my God,— why have you a - ban - doned me?———

Cm7   A°   Dm   B♭   Cm9 Fm   Gm   Dsus

Ped.

Richard T. Proulx

VERSES

Gm

Cantor/Choir

1. All who see me scoff at me;
(1.) "He relied on the LORD; let him de - liv - er him,

2. In - deed, many dogs sur - round me,
(2.) they have pierced my hands and my feet;

3. They di - vide my garments a - mong them,
(3.) But you, O LORD, be not far from me;

4. I will proclaim your name to my breth - ren;
(4.) "You who fear the LORD, praise him;

B♭   Gm

1. they mock me with parted lips, they wag their heads:
(1.) let him rescue him, if he loves him." **R/.**

2. a pack of evildoers closes in up - on me;
(2.) I can count all my bones. **R/.**

3. and for my ves - ture they cast lots.
(3.) O my help, has - ten to aid me. **R/.**

4. in the midst of the assembly I will praise you:
(4.) all you descendants of Jacob, give glory
to him; revere him, all you descendants of Is - ra - el!" **R/.**

Tone 2

Palm Sunday of the Lord's Passion, at the Mass   B30
Gospel Acclamation

RESPONSE

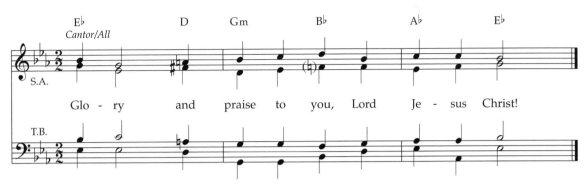

Glo - ry and praise to you, Lord Je - sus Christ!

Music © 1981, WLP

Adapt. from the Gregorian chant *Christus factus est* by Nicholas T. Freund

VERSE: *Philippians 2:8–9*

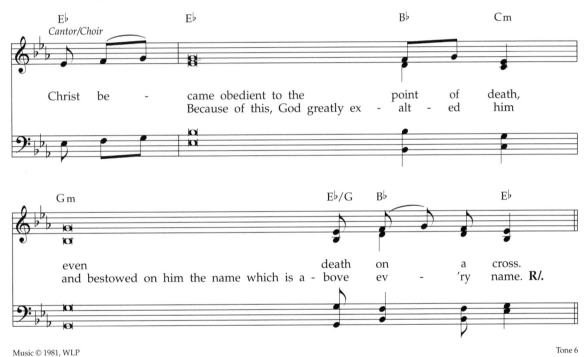

Christ be - came obedient to the point of death,
Because of this, God greatly ex - alt - ed him

even death on a cross.
and bestowed on him the name which is a - bove ev - 'ry name. **R/.**

Music © 1981, WLP

Tone 6

B31 Monday of Holy Week
Psalm 27:1, 2, 3, 13–14

RESPONSE: *Psalm 27:1a*

James M. Burns

VERSES

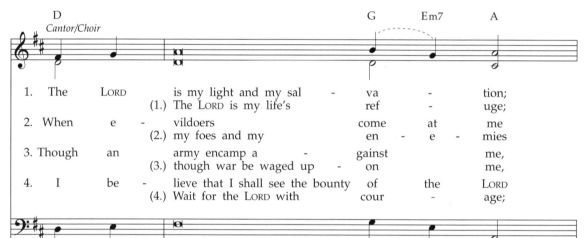

1. The LORD is my light and my sal - va - tion;
(1.) The LORD is my life's ref - uge;
2. When e - vildoers come at me
(2.) my foes and my en - e - mies
3. Though an army encamp a - gainst me,
(3.) though war be waged up - on me,
4. I be - lieve that I shall see the bounty of the LORD
(4.) Wait for the LORD with cour - age;

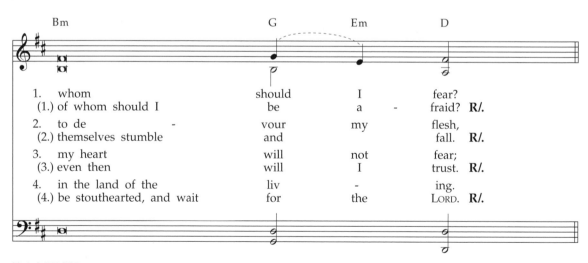

1. whom should I fear?
(1.) of whom should I be a - fraid? R/.
2. to de - vour my flesh,
(2.) themselves stumble and fall. R/.
3. my heart will not fear;
(3.) even then will I trust. R/.
4. in the land of the liv - ing.
(4.) be stouthearted, and wait for the LORD. R/.

James M. Burns

RESPONSE: *cf. Psalm 71:15ab*

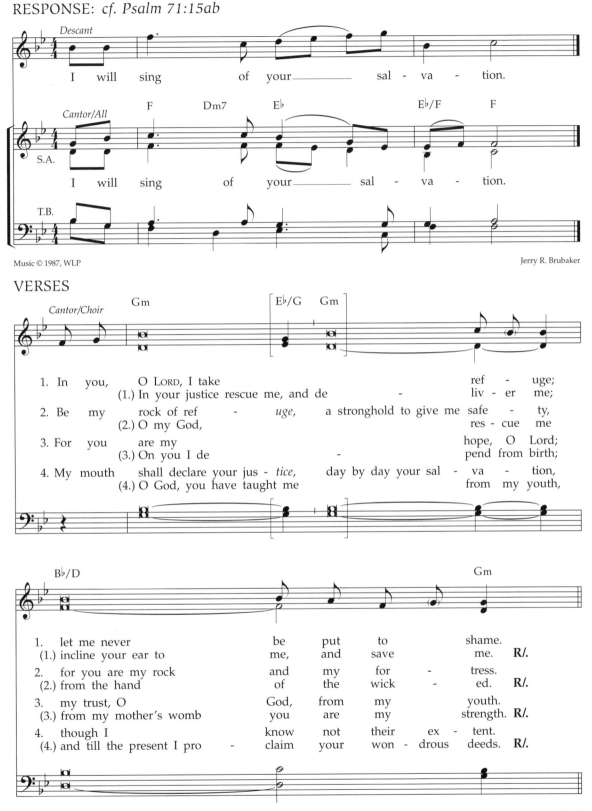

Music © 1987, WLP

Jerry R. Brubaker

VERSES

1. In you, O Lord, I take ref - uge;
   (1.) In your justice rescue me, and de - liv - er me;
2. Be my rock of ref - uge, a stronghold to give me safe - ty,
   (2.) O my God, res - cue me
3. For you are my hope, O Lord;
   (3.) On you I de - pend from birth;
4. My mouth shall declare your jus - tice, day by day your sal - va - tion,
   (4.) O God, you have taught me from my youth,

1. let me never be put to shame.
   (1.) incline your ear to me, and save me. **R/.**
2. for you are my rock and my for - tress.
   (2.) from the hand of the wick - ed. **R/.**
3. my trust, O God, from my youth.
   (3.) from my mother's womb you are my strength. **R/.**
4. though I know not their ex - tent.
   (4.) and till the present I pro - claim your won - drous deeds. **R/.**

Music © 2000, WLP

Tone 2

B33 Wednesday of Holy Week
Psalm 69:8–10, 14, 21–22, 31, 33–34

RESPONSE: *Psalm 69:14*

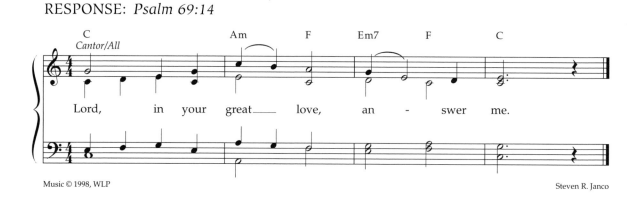

Lord, in your great love, answer me.

Music © 1998, WLP   Steven R. Janco

VERSES

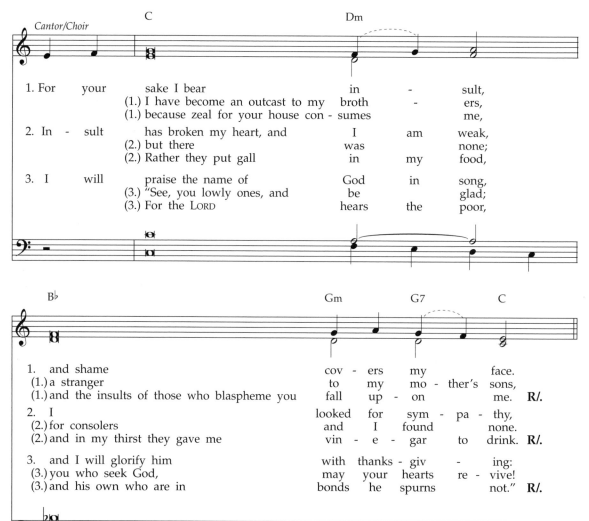

1. For your sake I bear insult,
(1.) I have become an outcast to my brothers,
(1.) because zeal for your house consumes me,

2. Insult has broken my heart, and I am weak,
(2.) but there was none;
(2.) Rather they put gall in my food,

3. I will praise the name of God in song,
(3.) "See, you lowly ones, and be glad;
(3.) For the Lord hears the poor,

1. and shame covers my face.
(1.) a stranger to my mother's sons,
(1.) and the insults of those who blaspheme you fall upon me. **R/.**

2. I looked for sympathy,
(2.) for consolers and I found none.
(2.) and in my thirst they gave me vinegar to drink. **R/.**

3. and I will glorify him with thanksgiving:
(3.) you who seek God, may your hearts revive!
(3.) and his own who are in bonds he spurns not." **R/.**

Music © 1984, WLP   Donald J. Reagan

Thursday of Holy Week—Chrism Mass   B34
Psalm 89:21–22, 25, 27

RESPONSE: *Psalm 89:2a*

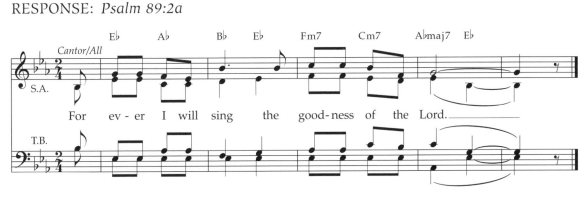

For ev-er I will sing the good-ness of the Lord.

Music © 1984, WLP

Robert E. Kreutz, 1922–1996

VERSES

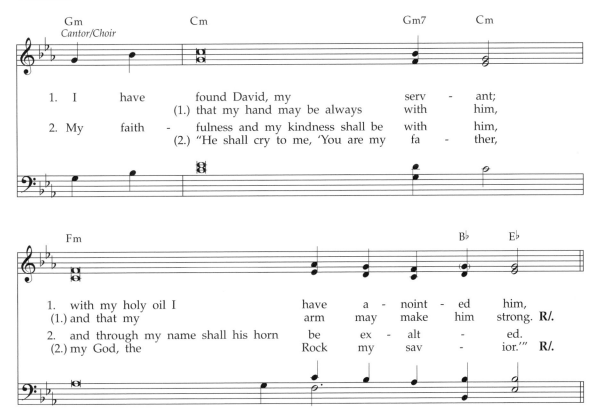

1. I have found David, my serv - ant;
(1.) that my hand may be always with him,
2. My faith - fulness and my kindness shall be with him,
(2.) "He shall cry to me, 'You are my fa - ther,

1. with my holy oil I have a - noint - ed him,
(1.) and that my arm may make him strong. **R/.**
2. and through my name shall his horn be ex - alt - ed.
(2.) my God, the Rock my sav - ior.'" **R/.**

Music © 1982, WLP

Robert E. Kreutz, 1922–1996

RESPONSE: *cf. 1 Corinthians 10:16*

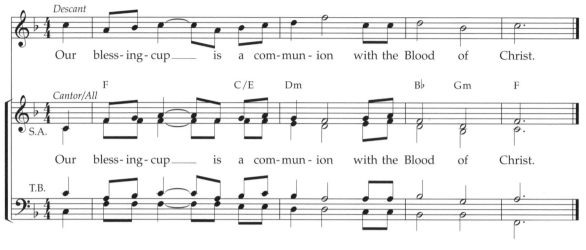

Music © 1994, WLP

Marcy Weckler

VERSES

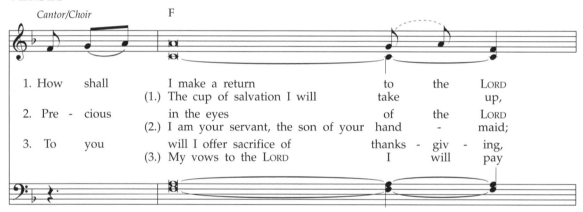

Music © 2000, WLP

Tone 6

Good Friday of the Lord's Passion
Psalm 31:2, 6, 12–13, 15–16, 17, 25

RESPONSE: *Luke 23:46*

Music © 1999, WLP

Howard Hughes

VERSES

1. In you, O Lord, I take ref - uge; let me never be put to shame.
   (1.) Into your hands I commend my spir - it;
2. For all my foes I am an object of reproach, a laughingstock to my neigh-*bors,* and a dread to my friends;
   (2.) I am forgotten like the unre - mem-bered dead;
3. But my trust is in you, O Lord;
   (3.) In your hands is my destiny; res - cue me
4. Let your face shine upon your serv - ant;
   (4.) Take courage and be stout - heart - ed,

1. In your jus - tice res - cue me.
   (1.) you will redeem me, O Lord, O faith - ful God. **R/.**
2. they who see me a - broad flee from me.
   (2.) I am like a dish that is bro - ken. **R/.**
3. I say, "You are my God.
   (3.) from the clutches of my enemies and my per - se - cu - tors." **R/.**
4. save me in your kind - ness.
   (4.) all you who hope in the Lord. **R/.**

Music © 2000, WLP

Tone 2

B37 Good Friday of the Lord's Passion
Veneration of the Cross

SHOWING THE CROSS

Sung three times.

Celebrant

This is the wood— of the cross, on which hung— the Sav - ior of the world.

Bm   C   G

All

Come, let us wor - ship.

SONG AT THE VENERATION

ANTIPHON

Cantor/All

We wor - ship you, Lord,____ we ven - er - ate your cross,____
we praise— your res - ur - rec - tion. Through the cross— you brought joy to the world.

VERSE: *Psalm 67:2*

Cantor/Choir   *To Antiphon*

May God be gra - cious and bless— us; and let his face shed its light— up - on us.

Sacramentary, 1974

BLESSING OF FIRE AND LIGHTING THE CANDLE

After the lighting of the Easter candle; sung three times.

Chant

Easter Proclamation   B39

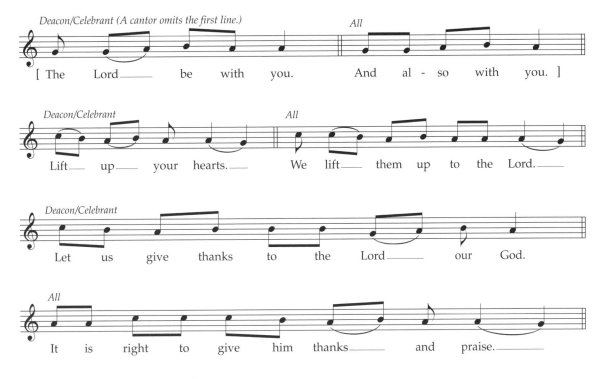

[The Lord be with you. And al - so with you.]

Lift up your hearts. We lift them up to the Lord.

Let us give thanks to the Lord our God.

It is right to give him thanks and praise.

It is truly right...for ever and ever.

A - men.

Sacramentary, 1974

[B40 is not needed in this revised edition.]

B41 Easter Vigil — First Reading
Psalm 104:1–2, 5–6, 10, 12, 13–14, 24, 35

RESPONSE: *Psalm 104:30*

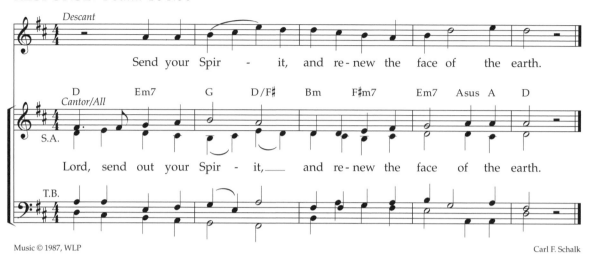

Send your Spir - it, and re - new the face of the earth.

Lord, send out your Spir - it,___ and re - new the face of the earth.

Carl F. Schalk

VERSES

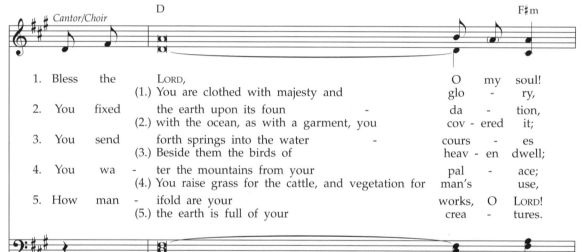

1. Bless the LORD, O my soul!
(1.) You are clothed with majesty and glo - ry,
2. You fixed the earth upon its foun - da - tion,
(2.) with the ocean, as with a garment, you cov - ered it;
3. You send forth springs into the water - cours - es
(3.) Beside them the birds of heav - en dwell;
4. You wa - ter the mountains from your pal - ace;
(4.) You raise grass for the cattle, and vegetation for man's use,
5. How man - ifold are your works, O LORD!
(5.) the earth is full of your crea - tures.

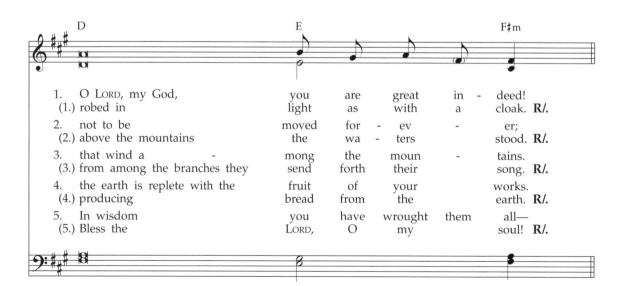

1. O LORD, my God, you are great in - deed!
(1.) robed in light as with a cloak. R/.
2. not to be moved for - ev - er;
(2.) above the mountains the wa - ters stood. R/.
3. that wind a - mong the moun - tains.
(3.) from among the branches they send forth their song. R/.
4. the earth is replete with the fruit of your works.
(4.) producing bread from the earth. R/.
5. In wisdom you have wrought them all—
(5.) Bless the LORD, O my soul! R/.

Tone 5

Easter Vigil — First Reading Alternative   B42
Psalm 33:4–7, 12–13, 20–22

RESPONSE: *Psalm 33:5*

The earth is full of the good-ness of the Lord.

Music © 1984, WLP   Howard L. Hughes

VERSES

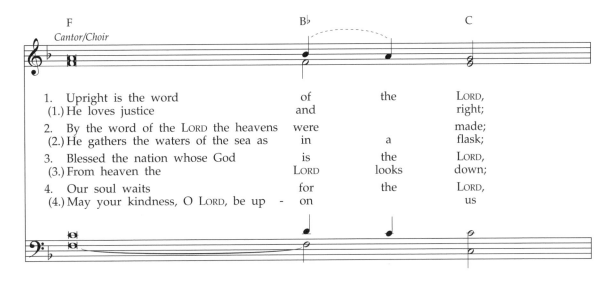

1. Upright is the word   of   the   LORD,
(1.) He loves justice   and   right;
2. By the word of the LORD the heavens   were   made;
(2.) He gathers the waters of the sea as   in   a   flask;
3. Blessed the nation whose God   is   the   LORD,
(3.) From heaven the   LORD   looks   down;
4. Our soul waits   for   the   LORD,
(4.) May your kindness, O LORD, be up - on   us

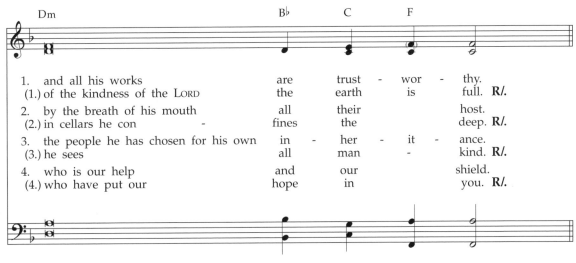

1. and all his works   are   trust - wor - thy.
(1.) of the kindness of the LORD   the   earth   is   full. **R/.**
2. by the breath of his mouth   all   their   host.
(2.) in cellars he con -   fines   the   deep. **R/.**
3. the people he has chosen for his own   in -   her - it - ance.
(3.) he sees   all   man -   kind. **R/.**
4. who is our help   and   our   shield.
(4.) who have put our   hope   in   you. **R/.**

Music © 1984, WLP   Howard L. Hughes

B43   Easter Vigil — Second Reading
Psalm 16:5, 8, 9–10, 11

RESPONSE: *Psalm 16:1*

Music © 1987, WLP

Paul A. Lisicky

VERSES

1. O LORD,   my allotted portion   and my cup,
(1.) I set the LORD ever be   -   fore me;
2. There - fore   my heart is glad and my soul re   -   joic - es,
(2.) because you will not abandon my soul to the   neth - er - world,
3. You will   show me the path to life, fullness of joys in your pres - ence,

1. you it is   who hold fast my lot.
(1.) with him at my right hand I   shall not be dis - turbed. **R/.**
2. my body, too, a   -   bides in con - fi - dence;
(2.) nor will you suffer your faithful one to under - go cor - rup - tion. **R/.**
3. the delights at your right   hand for - ev - er. **R/.**

Music © 2000, WLP

Tone 8c

Easter Vigil — Third Reading B44
Exodus 15:1–2, 3–4, 5–6, 17–18

RESPONSE: *Exodus 15:1*

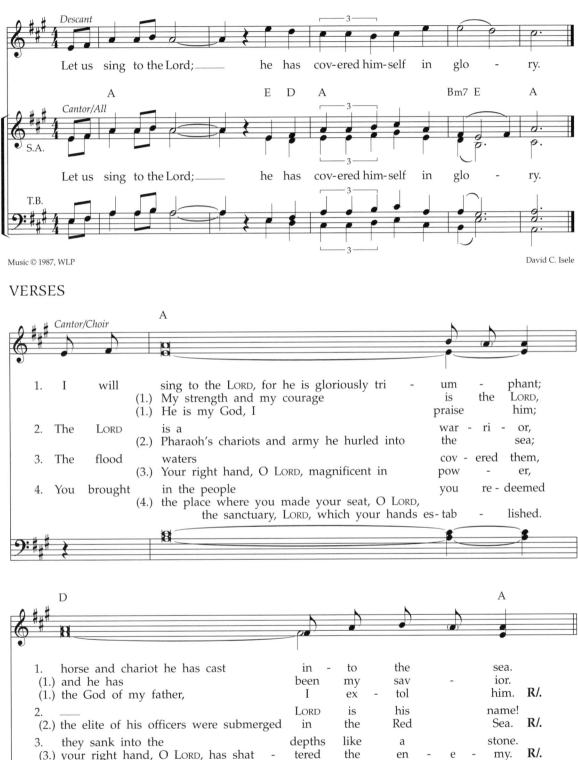

Music © 1987, WLP

David C. Isele

VERSES

1. I will sing to the LORD, for he is gloriously tri - um - phant;
   (1.) My strength and my courage is the LORD,
   (1.) He is my God, I praise him;
2. The LORD is a war - ri - or,
   (2.) Pharaoh's chariots and army he hurled into the sea;
3. The flood waters cov - ered them,
   (3.) Your right hand, O LORD, magnificent in pow - er,
4. You brought in the people you re - deemed
   (4.) the place where you made your seat, O LORD,
       the sanctuary, LORD, which your hands es - tab - lished.

1. horse and chariot he has cast in - to the sea.
   (1.) and he has been my sav - ior.
   (1.) the God of my father, I ex - tol him. **R/.**
2. __ LORD is his name!
   (2.) the elite of his officers were submerged in the Red Sea. **R/.**
3. they sank into the depths like a stone.
   (3.) your right hand, O LORD, has shat - tered the en - e - my. **R/.**
4. and planted them on the mountain of your in - her - it - ance—
   (4.) The LORD shall reign forev - er and ev - er. **R/.**

Music © 2000, WLP

Tone 8c

B45 Easter Vigil — Fourth Reading
Psalm 30:2, 4, 5–6, 11–12, 13

RESPONSE: *Psalm 30:2*

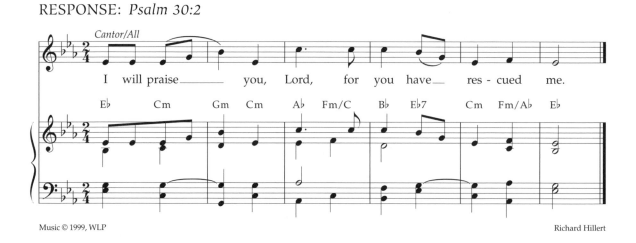

I will praise you, Lord, for you have res-cued me.

Music © 1999, WLP

Richard Hillert

VERSES

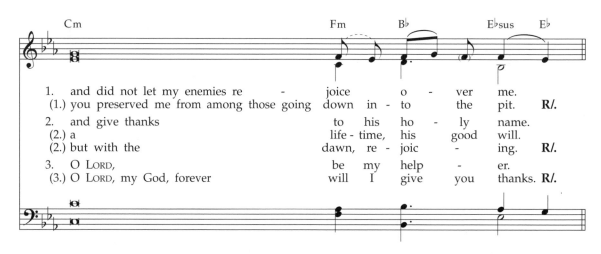

1. I will extol you, O LORD, for you drew me clear
(1.) O LORD, you brought me up from the neth - er - world;

2. Sing praise to the LORD, you his faith - ful ones,
(2.) For his anger lasts but a mo - ment;
(2.) At nightfall, weeping en - ters in,

3. Hear, O LORD, and have pity on me;
(3.) You changed my mourning into danc - ing;

1. and did not let my enemies re - joice o - ver me.
(1.) you preserved me from among those going down in - to the pit. **R/.**

2. and give thanks to his ho - ly name.
(2.) a life - time, his good will.
(2.) but with the dawn, re - joic - ing. **R/.**

3. O LORD, be my help - er.
(3.) O LORD, my God, forever will I give you thanks. **R/.**

Music © 1981, WLP

Tone 1f, adapt.

Easter Vigil — Fifth Reading B46
Isaiah 12:2–3, 4, 5–6

RESPONSE: *Isaiah 12:3*

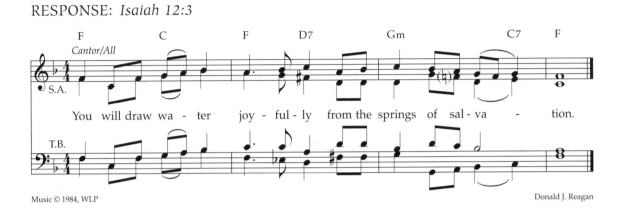

You will draw wa - ter joy - ful - ly from the springs of sal - va - tion.

Donald J. Reagan

VERSES

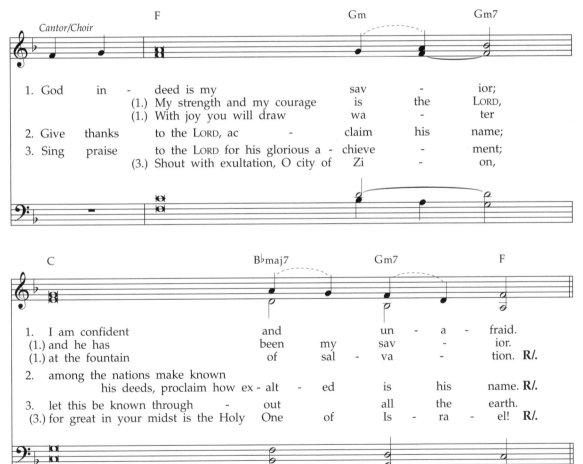

1. God in - deed is my sav - ior;
(1.) My strength and my courage is the LORD,
(1.) With joy you will draw wa - ter
2. Give thanks to the LORD, ac - claim his name;
3. Sing praise to the LORD for his glorious a - chieve - ment;
(3.) Shout with exultation, O city of Zi - on,

1. I am confident and un - a - fraid.
(1.) and he has been my sav - ior.
(1.) at the fountain of sal - va - tion. R/.
2. among the nations make known his deeds, proclaim how ex - alt - ed is his name. R/.
3. let this be known through - out all the earth.
(3.) for great in your midst is the Holy One of Is - ra - el! R/.

Donald J. Reagan

B47 Easter Vigil — Sixth Reading
Psalm 19:8, 9, 10, 11

RESPONSE: *John 6:68c*

Lord, you have the words of ev-er-last-ing life, the

Lord, you have the words___ of ev-er-last-ing___ life,___ the

words of ev-er-last - ing life.___

words of ev-er-last - ing life.___

Marty Haugen

VERSES

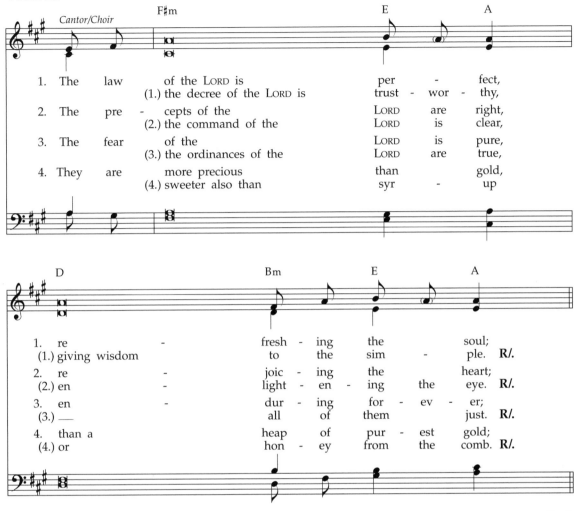

Music © 1972, WLP

Tone 8c

B48 Easter Vigil — Seventh Reading
Psalm 42:2–3, 5; 43:3, 4

RESPONSE: *Psalm 42:2*

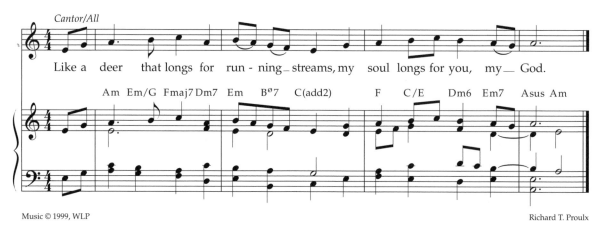

Like a deer that longs for run - ning streams, my soul longs for you, my God.

Richard T. Proulx

VERSES

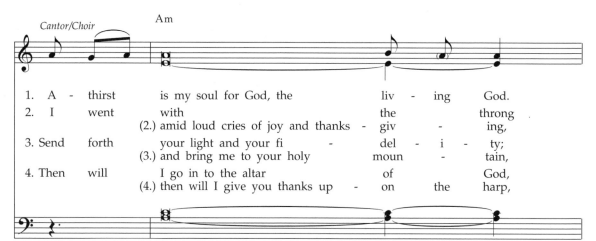

1. A - thirst is my soul for God, the liv - ing God.
2. I went with the throng
   (2.) amid loud cries of joy and thanks - giv - ing,
3. Send forth your light and your fi - del - i - ty;
   (3.) and bring me to your holy moun - tain,
4. Then will I go in to the altar of God,
   (4.) then will I give you thanks up - on the harp,

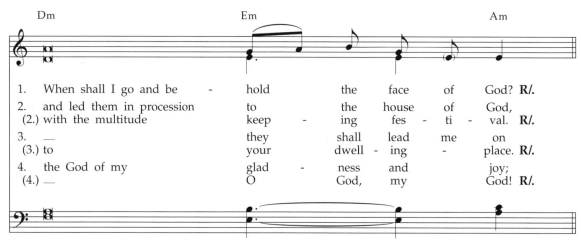

1. When shall I go and be - hold the face of God? **R/.**
2. and led them in procession to the house of God,
   (2.) with the multitude keep - ing fes - ti - val. **R/.**
3. — they shall lead me on
   (3.) to your dwell - ing - place. **R/.**
4. the God of my glad - ness and joy;
   (4.) — O God, my God! **R/.**

Tone 4A, adapt.

Easter Vigil — Seventh Reading Alternative
Psalm 51:12–13, 14–15, 18–19

RESPONSE: *Psalm 51:12*

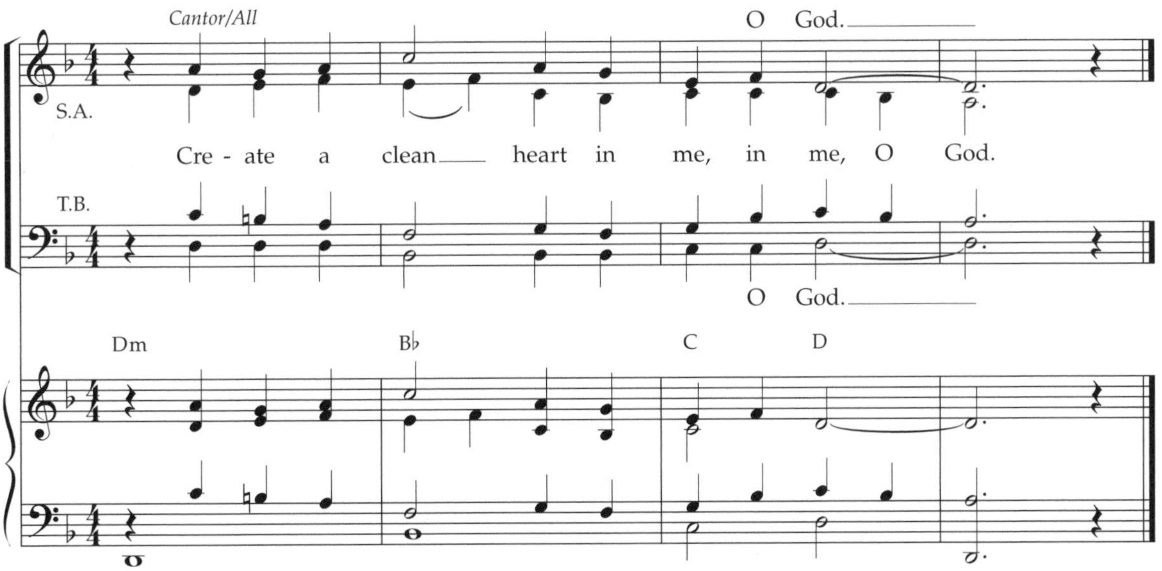

Music © 1999, WLP

Rory Cooney

VERSES

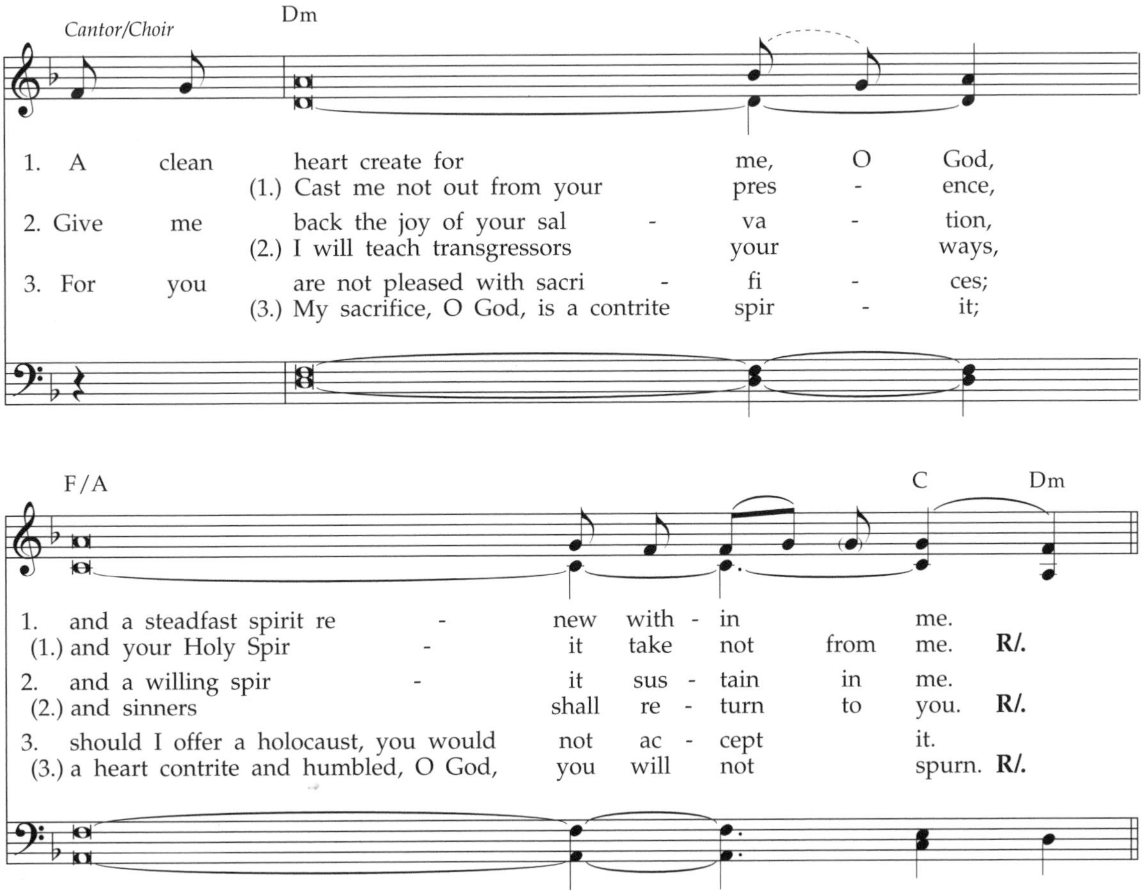

1. A clean heart create for me, O God,
(1.) Cast me not out from your pres - ence,
2. Give me back the joy of your sal - va - tion,
(2.) I will teach transgressors your ways,
3. For you are not pleased with sacri - fi - ces;
(3.) My sacrifice, O God, is a contrite spir - it;

1. and a steadfast spirit re - new with - in me. **R/.**
(1.) and your Holy Spir - it take not from me. **R/.**
2. and a willing spir - it sus - tain in me.
(2.) and sinners shall re - turn to you. **R/.**
3. should I offer a holocaust, you would not ac - cept it.
(3.) a heart contrite and humbled, O God, you will not spurn. **R/.**

Music © 2000, WLP

Tone 1f

RESPONSE

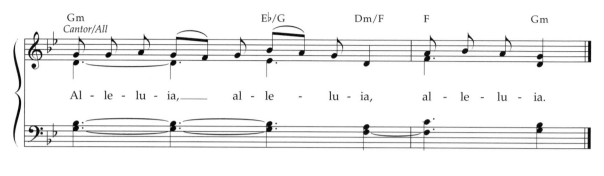

Mode II

VERSES

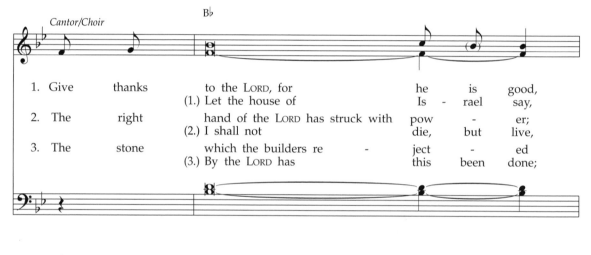

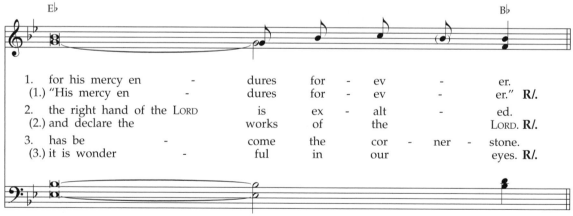

Tone 8c

Psalm 118:1–2, 16–17, 22–23

RESPONSE

Arr. by Nicholas T. Freund

VERSES

Nicholas T. Freund

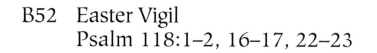

B52   Easter Vigil
Psalm 118:1–2, 16–17, 22–23

RESPONSE

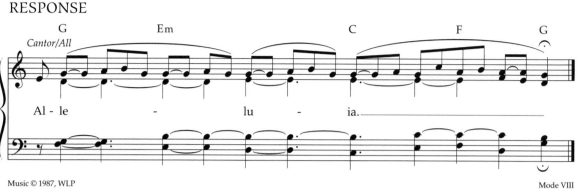

Music © 1987, WLP

Mode VIII
Acc. by Angelo A. della Picca

VERSES

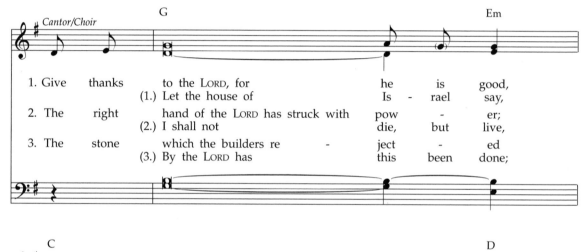

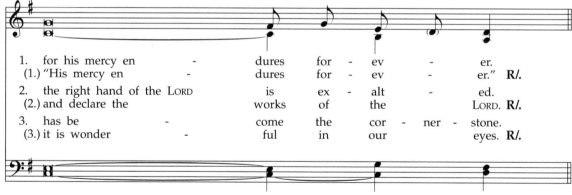

Music © 2000, WLP

Tone 8G

B53 Easter Sunday
Psalm 118:1–2, 16–17, 22–23

RESPONSE: *Psalm 118:24*

Music © 1994, WLP

Alan J. Hommerding

A sung Alleluia *may replace this response.*

VERSES*

Cantor/Choir

1. Give thanks to the LORD, for he is good, for his
2. "The right hand of the LORD has struck with pow'r; the
3. The stone which the build-ers re - ject - ed has be -

1. mer - cy en-dures for - ev - er. Let the house of
2. right hand of the LORD is ex - alt - ed." I shall not die, but
3. come the cor - ner - stone. By the LORD has

1. Is - ra-el say, "His mer-cy en-dures for - ev - er.
2. live, and de - clare the works of the LORD."
3. this been done; it is won - der - ful in our eyes.

To Response

Music © 1994, WLP

Alan J. Hommerding

Verses to psalm tone follow.

VERSES

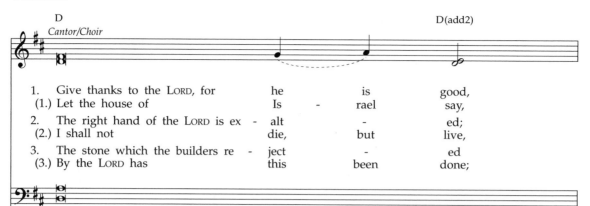

1. Give thanks to the LORD, for he is good,
(1.) Let the house of Is - rael say,
2. The right hand of the LORD is ex - alt - ed;
(2.) I shall not die, but live,
3. The stone which the builders re - ject - ed
(3.) By the LORD has this been done;

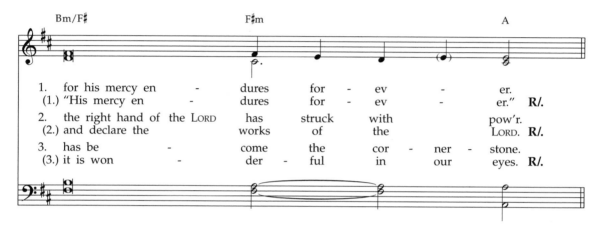

1. for his mercy en - dures for - ev - er.
(1.) "His mercy en - dures for - ev - er." R/.
2. the right hand of the LORD has struck with pow'r.
(2.) and declare the works of the LORD. R/.
3. has be - come the cor - ner - stone.
(3.) it is won - der - ful in our eyes. R/.

Alan J. Hommerding

[B54, B55, and B56 are not needed in this revised edition]

Easter Sunday   B57
Sequence—Lectionary Text

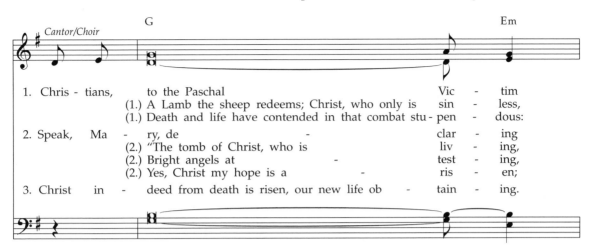

Cantor/Choir

1. Chris - tians,   to the Paschal   Vic - tim
   (1.) A Lamb the sheep redeems; Christ, who only is   sin - less,
   (1.) Death and life have contended in that combat stu - pen - dous:
2. Speak, Ma - ry, de -   clar - ing
   (2.) "The tomb of Christ, who is   liv - ing,
   (2.) Bright angels at -   test - ing,
   (2.) Yes, Christ my hope is a -   ris - en;
3. Christ in - deed from death is risen, our new life ob - tain - ing.

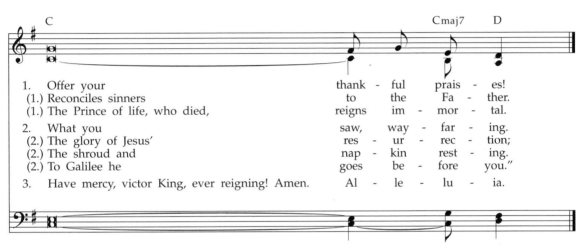

1. Offer your   thank - ful   prais - es!
   (1.) Reconciles sinners   to   the   Fa - ther.
   (1.) The Prince of life, who died,   reigns   im - mor - tal.
2. What you   saw, way - far - ing.
   (2.) The glory of Jesus'   res - ur - rec - tion;
   (2.) The shroud and   nap - kin rest - ing.
   (2.) To Galilee he   goes   be - fore   you."
3. Have mercy, victor King, ever reigning! Amen.   Al - le - lu - ia.

Music © 2000, WLP
Ascr. to Wipo of Burgundy, c. 1000–c. 1050
Tr. *The Antiphoner and Grail*, 1880, alt.

Tone 8G

B58 Second Sunday of Easter
Psalm 118:1–4, 13–15, 22–24

RESPONSE: *Psalm 118:1*

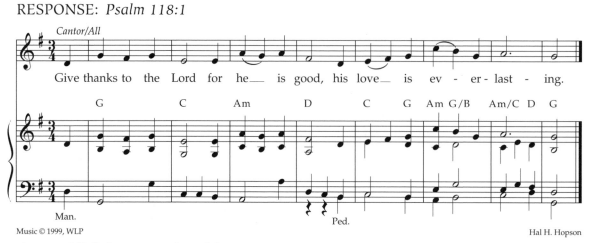

Give thanks to the Lord for he__ is good, his love__ is ev - er - last - ing.

Music © 1999, WLP

Hal H. Hopson

A sung Alleluia *may replace this response.*

VERSES

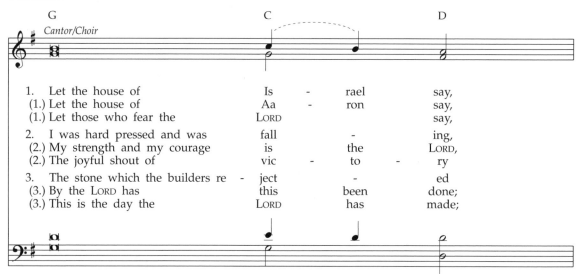

1. Let the house of   Is - rael   say,
(1.) Let the house of   Aa - ron   say,
(1.) Let those who fear the   LORD   say,

2. I was hard pressed and was   fall - ing,
(2.) My strength and my courage   is   the   LORD,
(2.) The joyful shout of   vic - to - ry

3. The stone which the builders re - ject - ed
(3.) By the LORD has   this   been   done;
(3.) This is the day the   LORD   has   made;

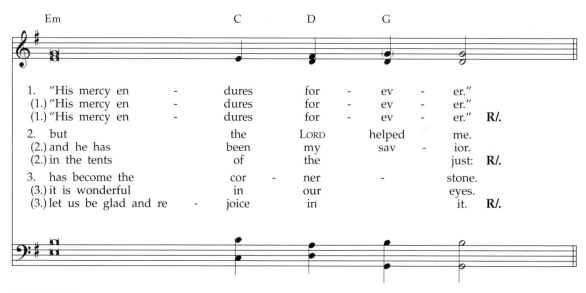

1. "His mercy en - dures for - ev - er."
(1.) "His mercy en - dures for - ev - er."
(1.) "His mercy en - dures for - ev - er." **R/.**

2. but   the   LORD   helped   me.
(2.) and he has   been   my   sav - ior.
(2.) in the tents   of   the   just: **R/.**

3. has become the   cor - ner - stone.
(3.) it is wonderful   in   our   eyes.
(3.) let us be glad and re - joice   in   it. **R/.**

Music © 1984, WLP

Howard L. Hughes

RESPONSE: *Psalm 4:7a*

Music © 1989, WLP

Michael Joncas

A sung Alleluia *may replace this response.*

VERSES

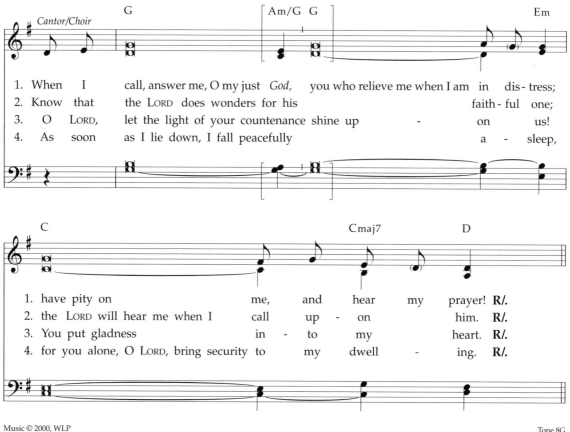

Music © 2000, WLP

Tone 8G

Fourth Sunday of Easter   B60
Psalm 118:1, 8–9, 21–23, 26, 28, 29

RESPONSE: *Psalm 118:22*

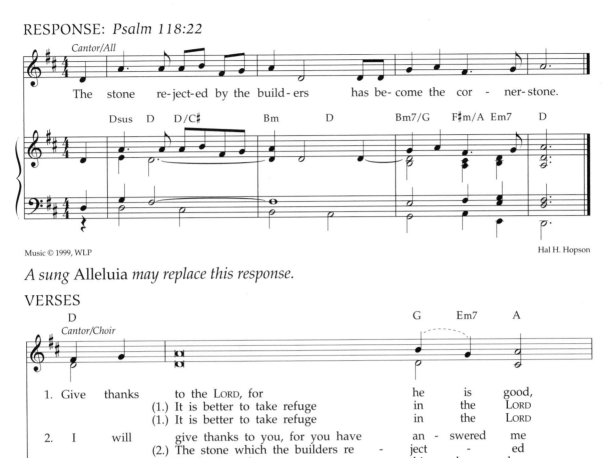

The stone re-ject-ed by the build-ers has be-come the cor - ner-stone.

Music © 1999, WLP

Hal H. Hopson

A sung Alleluia *may replace this response.*

VERSES

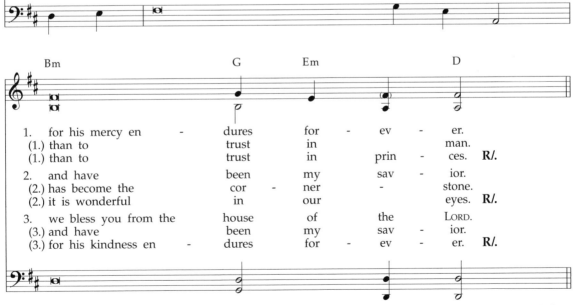

1. Give thanks to the LORD, for he is good,
   (1.) It is better to take refuge in the LORD
   (1.) It is better to take refuge in the LORD

2. I will give thanks to you, for you have an - swered me
   (2.) The stone which the builders re - ject - ed
   (2.) By the LORD has this been done;

3. Bless - ed is he who comes in the name of the LORD;
   (3.) I will give thanks to you, for you have an - swered me
   (3.) Give thanks to the LORD, for he is good;

1. for his mercy en - dures for - ev - er.
   (1.) than to trust in man.
   (1.) than to trust in prin - ces. **R/.**

2. and have been my sav - ior.
   (2.) has become the cor - ner - stone.
   (2.) it is wonderful in our eyes. **R/.**

3. we bless you from the house of the LORD.
   (3.) and have been my sav - ior.
   (3.) for his kindness en - dures for - ev - er. **R/.**

Music © 1984, WLP

James M. Burns

Fifth Sunday of Easter
Psalm 22:26-27, 28, 30, 31–32

RESPONSE: *Psalm 22:26a*

Music © 1999, WLP

Steven C. Warner

A sung Alleluia *may replace this response.*

VERSES

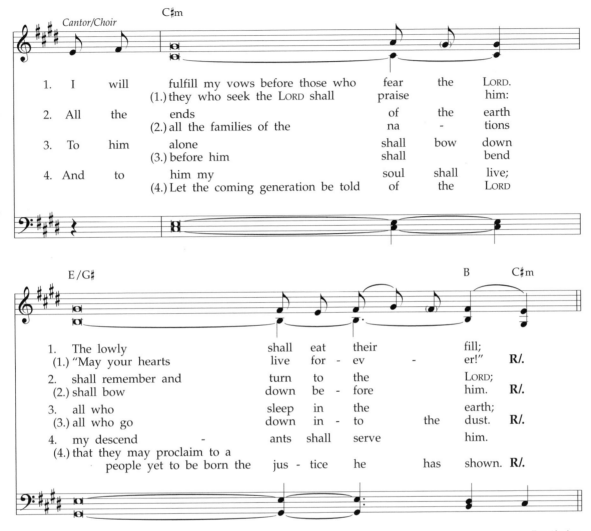

Music © 2000, WLP

Tone 1f, adapt.

B62 Sixth Sunday of Easter
Psalm 98:1, 2–3, 3–4

RESPONSE: *cf. Psalm 98:2b*

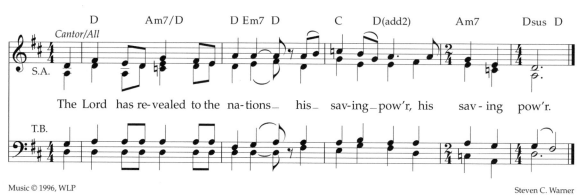

The Lord has re-vealed to the na-tions his sav-ing pow'r, his sav-ing pow'r.

Music © 1996, WLP

Steven C. Warner

A sung Alleluia *may replace this response.*

VERSES

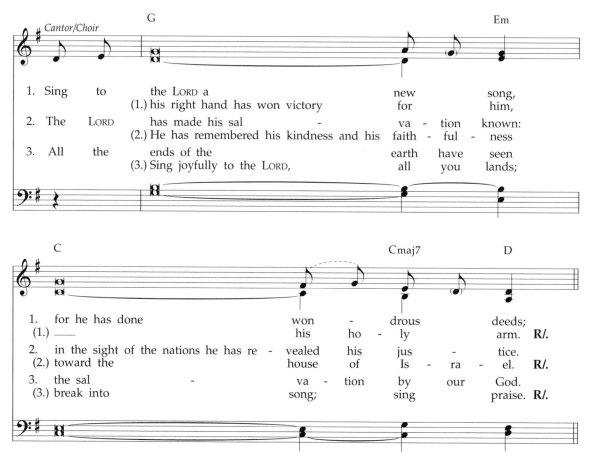

1. Sing to the LORD a new song,
(1.) his right hand has won victory for him,
2. The LORD has made his sal - va - tion known:
(2.) He has remembered his kindness and his faith - ful - ness
3. All the ends of the earth have seen
(3.) Sing joyfully to the LORD, all you lands;

1. for he has done won - drous deeds;
(1.) —— his ho - ly arm. **R/.**
2. in the sight of the nations he has re - vealed his jus - tice.
(2.) toward the house of Is - ra - el. **R/.**
3. the sal - va - tion by our God.
(3.) break into song; sing praise. **R/.**

Music © 2000, WLP

Tone 8G

B63 The Ascension of the Lord
Revised
Psalm 47:2–3, 6–7, 8–9

RESPONSE: *Psalm 47:6*

God mounts his throne to shouts of joy; a blare of trum-pets for the Lord.

Michel Guimont

A sung Alleluia *may replace this response.*

VERSES

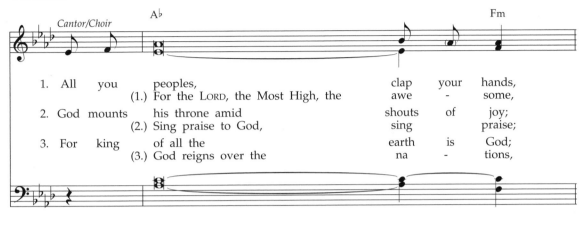

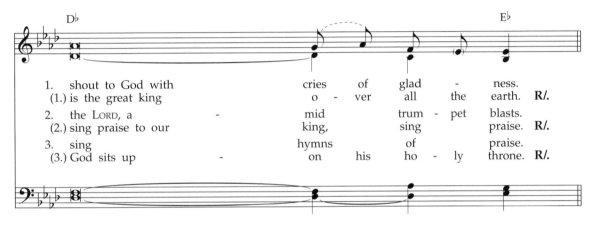

Music © 2000, WLP

Tone 8G

RESPONSE: *Psalm 103:19a*

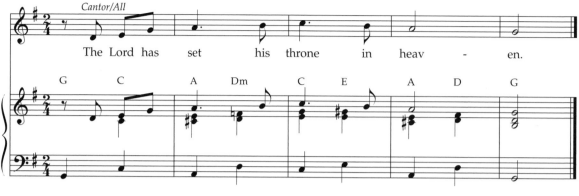

Music © 1999, WLP   Richard Hillert

A sung Alleluia *may replace this response.*

VERSES

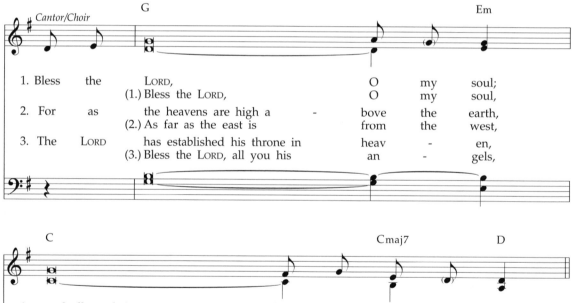

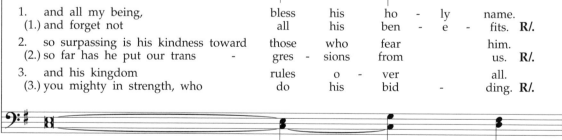

Music © 2000, WLP   Tone 8G

Pentecost Sunday, at the Vigil Mass   B65
Psalm 104:1–2, 24, 35, 27–28, 30

RESPONSE: *cf. Psalm 104:30*

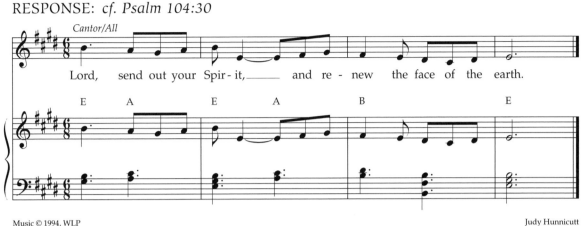

Lord, send out your Spir-it, and re-new the face of the earth.

Music © 1994, WLP

Judy Hunnicutt

A sung Alleluia *may replace this response.*

VERSES

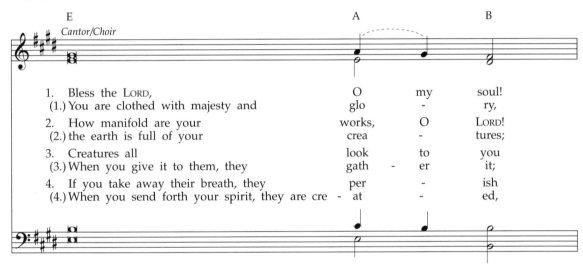

1. Bless the LORD, O my soul!
(1.) You are clothed with majesty and glo - ry,

2. How manifold are your works, O LORD!
(2.) the earth is full of your crea - tures;

3. Creatures all look to you
(3.) When you give it to them, they gath - er it;

4. If you take away their breath, they per - ish
(4.) When you send forth your spirit, they are cre - at - ed,

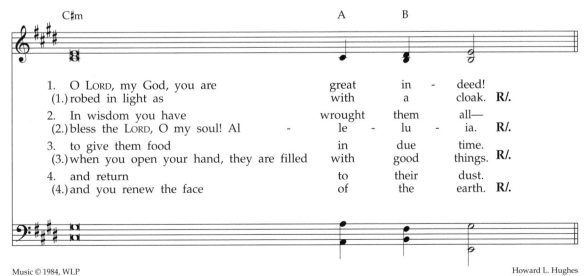

1. O LORD, my God, you are great in - deed!
(1.) robed in light as with a cloak. **R/.**

2. In wisdom you have wrought them all—
(2.) bless the LORD, O my soul! Al - le - lu - ia. **R/.**

3. to give them food in due time.
(3.) when you open your hand, they are filled with good things. **R/.**

4. and return to their dust.
(4.) and you renew the face of the earth. **R/.**

Music © 1984, WLP

Howard L. Hughes

B66 Pentecost Sunday, Mass during the Day
Psalm 104:1, 24, 29–31, 34

RESPONSE: *cf. Psalm 104:30*

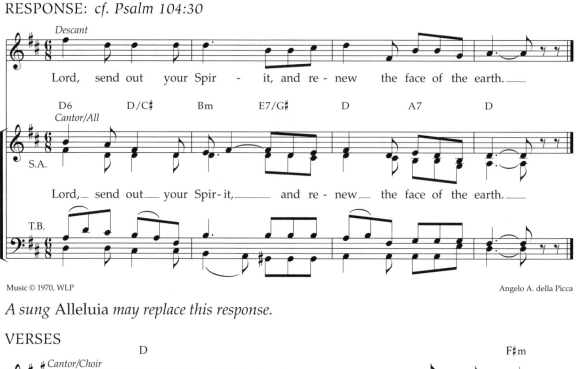

Descant

Lord, send out your Spir - it, and re - new the face of the earth.____

D6   D/C♯   Bm   E7/G♯   D   A7   D

Cantor/All

S.A.

Lord,__ send out__ your Spir- it,_____ and re - new__ the face of the earth.____

T.B.

Music © 1970, WLP   Angelo A. della Picca

A sung Alleluia *may replace this response.*

VERSES

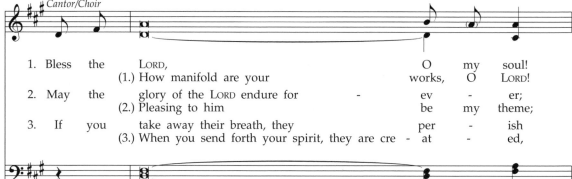

D   F♯m

Cantor/Choir

1. Bless the LORD,   O my soul!
(1.) How manifold are your   works, O LORD!
2. May the glory of the LORD endure for - ev - er;
(2.) Pleasing to him   be my theme;
3. If you take away their breath, they   per - ish
(3.) When you send forth your spirit, they are cre - at - ed,

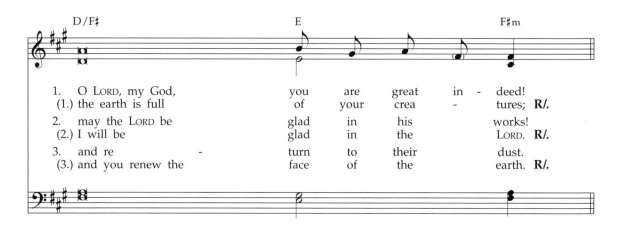

D/F♯   E   F♯m

1. O LORD, my God,   you are great in - deed!
(1.) the earth is full   of your crea - tures; **R/.**
2. may the LORD be   glad in his works!
(2.) I will be   glad in the LORD. **R/.**
3. and re - turn to their dust.
(3.) and you renew the   face of the earth. **R/.**

Music © 2000, WLP   Tone 5

Pentecost Sunday, Mass during the Day
Sequence

G   Am/G   G   Em

1. Come, Ho - ly Spirit, come! And from your ce - les - tial home
2. Come, Fa - ther of the poor! Come, source of all our store!
3. You, of comforters the best; You, the soul's most wel- come guest;

4. In our labor, rest most sweet; Grateful coolness in the heat;
5. O most blessed Light di - vine, Shine within these hearts of yours,

C   Cmaj7   D

1. Shed a ray of light di - vine!
2. Come, with - in our bo - soms shine.
3. Sweet re - fresh - ment here be - low;

4. Solace in the midst of woe.
5. And our in - most be - ing fill!

G   Am/G   G   Em

6. Where you are not, we have naught, Nothing good in deed or thought,
7. Heal our wounds, our strength re-new; On our dryness pour your dew;
8. Bend the stubborn heart and will; Melt the frozen, warm the chill;

9. On the faithful, who a - dore And confess you, ev - er - more
10. Give them virtue's sure re - ward; Give them your sal - va - tion, Lord;

C   Cmaj7   D

6. Nothing free from taint of ill.
7. Wash the stains of guilt a - way:
8. Guide the steps that go a - stray.

9. In your sev'n - fold gift de - scend;
10. Give them joys that never end. A - men. Al - le - lu - ia.

Music © 2000, WLP

Tone 8G

[B68 is not needed in this revised edition.]

B69 The Solemnity of the Most Holy Trinity
Psalm 33:4–6, 9, 12, 18–19, 20, 22

RESPONSE: *Psalm 33:12b*

Descant

Bless - ed the peo - ple the Lord has cho - sen to

Cantor/All

S.A.

Bless - ed the peo - ple the Lord___ has cho - sen to

T.B.

be his own, to be___ his own.

be his own, to be___ his own.

Howard L. Hughes

VERSES

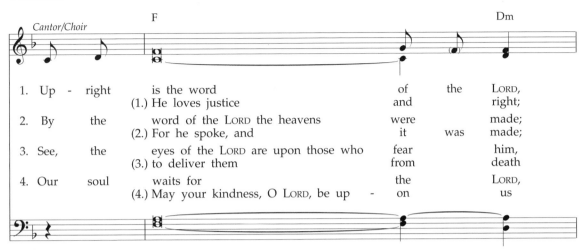

1. Up - right is the word of the LORD,
   (1.) He loves justice and right;
2. By the word of the LORD the heavens were made;
   (2.) For he spoke, and it was made;
3. See, the eyes of the LORD are upon those who fear him,
   (3.) to deliver them from death
4. Our soul waits for the LORD,
   (4.) May your kindness, O LORD, be up - on us

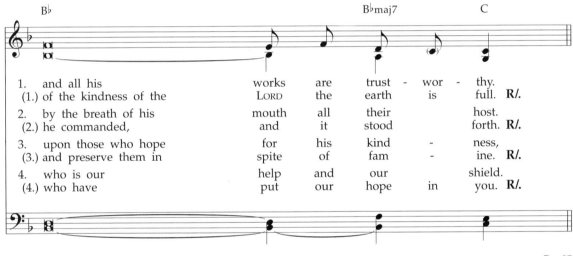

1. and all his works are trust - wor - thy.
   (1.) of the kindness of the LORD the earth is full. **R/.**
2. by the breath of his mouth all their host.
   (2.) he commanded, and it stood forth. **R/.**
3. upon those who hope for his kind - ness,
   (3.) and preserve them in spite of fam - ine. **R/.**
4. who is our help and our shield.
   (4.) who have put our hope in you. **R/.**

Tone 8G

B70 The Solemnity of the Most Holy Body and Blood of Christ
Psalm 116:12–13, 15–16, 17–18

RESPONSE: *Psalm 116:13*

I will take the cup of sal-va-tion, and__ call on the name of the Lord.

Music © 1996, WLP

Steven R. Janco

A sung Alleluia *may replace this response.*

VERSES

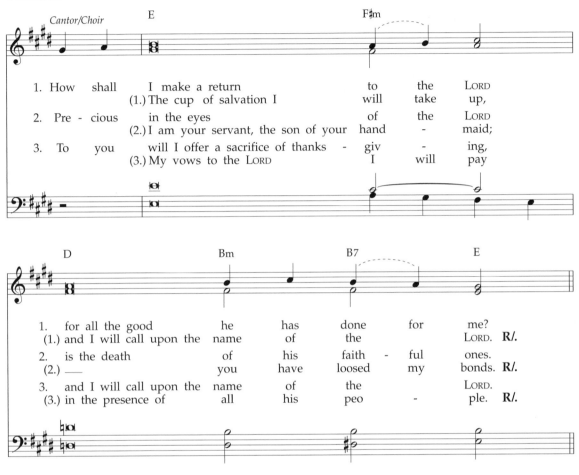

Donald J. Reagan

B70a The Solemnity of the Most Holy Body
Revised
and Blood of Christ
Sequence

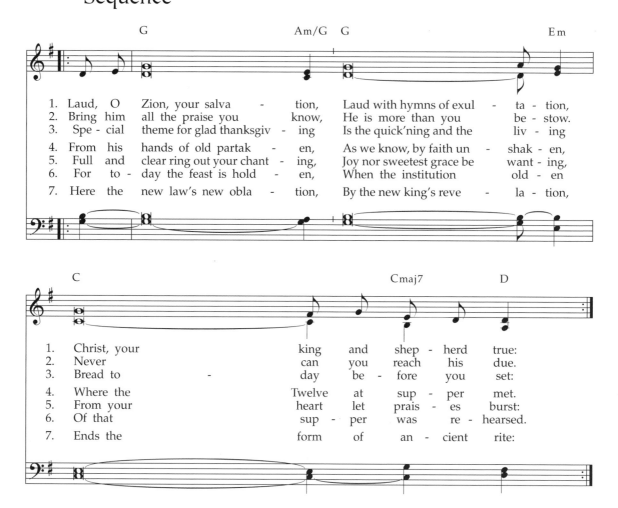

1. Laud, O Zion, your salva - tion, Laud with hymns of exul - ta - tion,
2. Bring him all the praise you know, He is more than you be - stow.
3. Spe - cial theme for glad thanksgiv - ing Is the quick'ning and the liv - ing
4. From his hands of old partak - en, As we know, by faith un - shak - en,
5. Full and clear ring out your chant - ing, Joy nor sweetest grace be want - ing,
6. For to - day the feast is hold - en, When the institution old - en
7. Here the new law's new obla - tion, By the new king's reve - la - tion,

1. Christ, your king and shep - herd true:
2. Never can you reach his due.
3. Bread to - day be - fore you set:
4. Where the Twelve at sup - per met.
5. From your heart let prais - es burst:
6. Of that sup - per was re - hearsed.
7. Ends the form of an - cient rite:

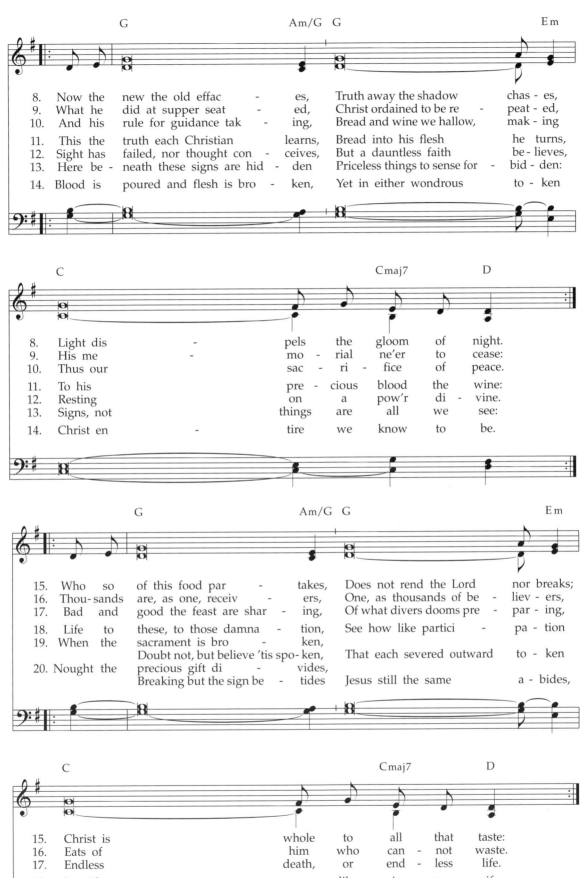

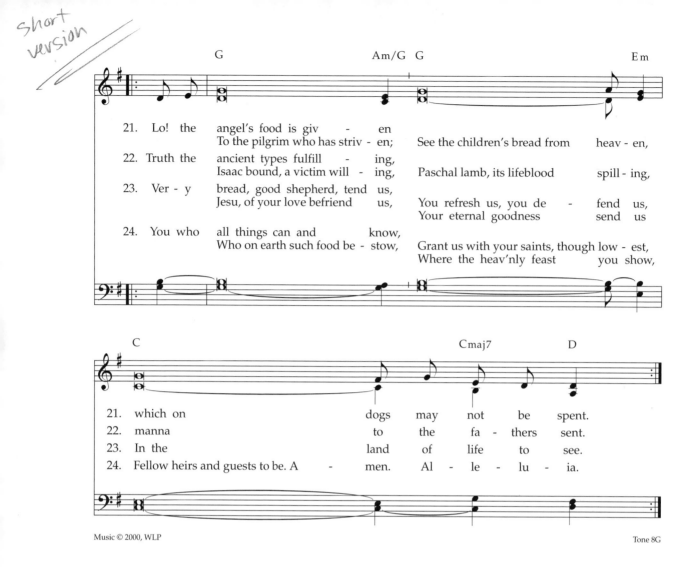

21. Lo! the angel's food is giv - en
To the pilgrim who has striv - en; See the children's bread from heav - en,
22. Truth the ancient types fulfill - ing,
Isaac bound, a victim will - ing, Paschal lamb, its lifeblood spill - ing,
23. Ver - y bread, good shepherd, tend us,
Jesu, of your love befriend us, You refresh us, you de - fend us,
Your eternal goodness send us
24. You who all things can and know,
Who on earth such food be - stow, Grant us with your saints, though low - est,
Where the heav'nly feast you show,

21. which on dogs may not be spent.
22. manna to the fa - thers sent.
23. In the land of life to see.
24. Fellow heirs and guests to be. A - men. Al - le - lu - ia.

Tone 8G

The Solemnity of the Most Sacred Heart of Jesus   B71
Isaiah 12:2–3, 4, 5–6

RESPONSE: *Isaiah 12:3*

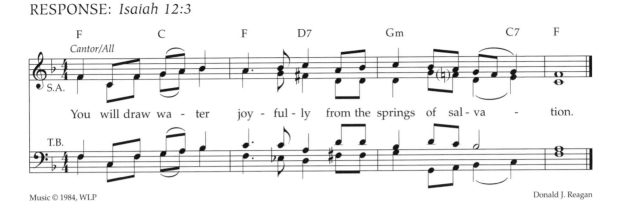

You will draw wa - ter joy - ful - ly from the springs of sal - va - tion.

Music © 1984, WLP

Donald J. Reagan

VERSES

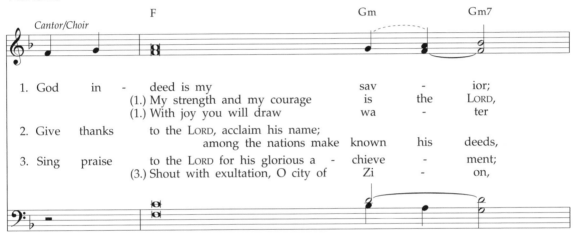

Cantor/Choir

1. God in - deed is my sav - ior;
(1.) My strength and my courage is the LORD,
(1.) With joy you will draw wa - ter

2. Give thanks to the LORD, acclaim his name;
among the nations make known his deeds,

3. Sing praise to the LORD for his glorious a - chieve - ment;
(3.) Shout with exultation, O city of Zi - on,

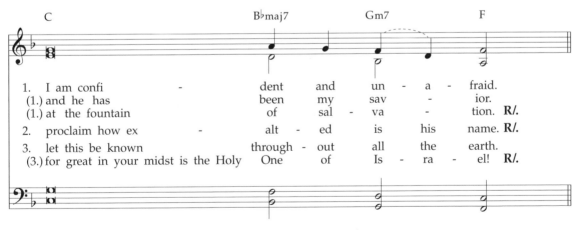

1. I am confi - dent and un - a - fraid.
(1.) and he has been my sav - ior.
(1.) at the fountain of sal - va - tion. **R/.**

2. proclaim how ex - alt - ed is his name. **R/.**

3. let this be known through - out all the earth.
(3.) for great in your midst is the Holy One of Is - ra - el! **R/.**

Music © 1984, WLP

Donald J. Reagan

B72 Second Sunday in Ordinary Time
Psalm 40:2, 4, 7–8, 8–9, 10

RESPONSE: *Psalm 40:8a, 9a*

Here am I, Lord;_____ I come to do__ your will.

Music © 1998, WLP

Donna B. Kasbohm

VERSES

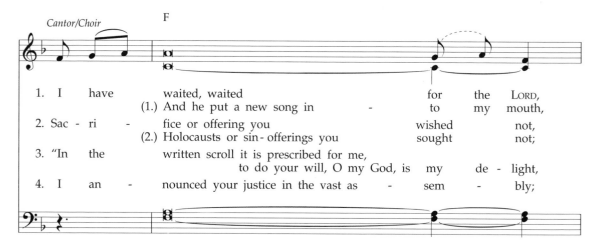

1. I have waited, waited for the LORD,
(1.) And he put a new song in - to my mouth,
2. Sac - ri - fice or offering you wished not,
(2.) Holocausts or sin - offerings you sought not;
3. "In the written scroll it is prescribed for me,
to do your will, O my God, is my de - light,
4. I an - nounced your justice in the vast as - sem - bly;

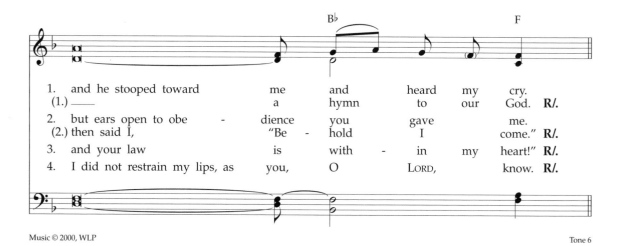

1. and he stooped toward me and heard my cry.
(1.) _____ a hymn to our God. **R/.**
2. but ears open to obe - dience you gave me.
(2.) then said I, "Be - hold I come." **R/.**
3. and your law is with - in my heart!" **R/.**
4. I did not restrain my lips, as you, O LORD, know. **R/.**

Music © 2000, WLP

Tone 6

Third Sunday in Ordinary Time   B73
Psalm 25:4–5, 6–7, 8–9

RESPONSE: *Psalm 25:4a*

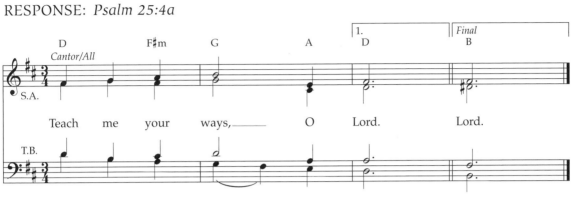

Teach me your ways,⸺ O Lord. Lord.

Music © 1972, WLP

Robert E. Kreutz, 1922–1996

VERSES

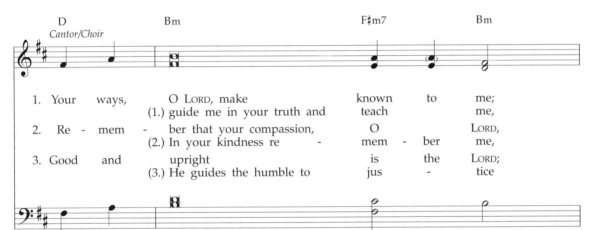

1. Your ways, O Lord, make known to me;
(1.) guide me in your truth and teach me,
2. Re - mem - ber that your compassion, O Lord,
(2.) In your kindness re - mem - ber me,
3. Good and upright is the Lord;
(3.) He guides the humble to jus - tice

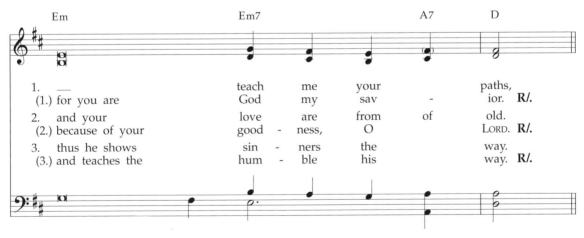

1. ⸺ teach me your paths,
(1.) for you are God my sav - ior. **R/.**
2. and your love are from of old.
(2.) because of your good - ness, O Lord. **R/.**
3. thus he shows sin - ners the way.
(3.) and teaches the hum - ble his way. **R/.**

Music © 1982, WLP

Robert E. Kreutz, 1922–1996

B74 Fourth Sunday in Ordinary Time
Psalm 95:1–2, 6–7, 7–9

RESPONSE: *Psalm 95:8*

Music © 1994, WLP

Jeffrey Honoré

VERSES

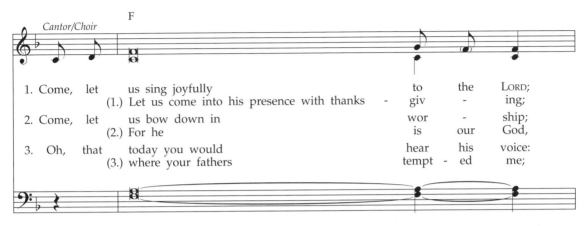

Cantor/Choir

F

1. Come, let us sing joyfully to the LORD;
   (1.) Let us come into his presence with thanks - giv - ing;
2. Come, let us bow down in wor - ship;
   (2.) For he is our God,
3. Oh, that today you would hear his voice:
   (3.) where your fathers tempt - ed me;

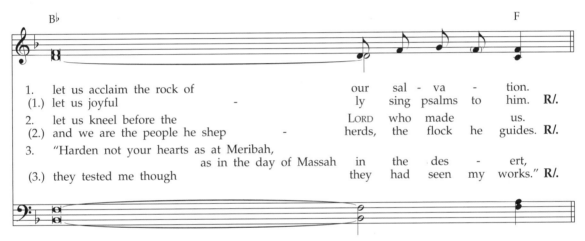

B♭   F

1. let us acclaim the rock of our sal - va - tion.
   (1.) let us joyful - ly sing psalms to him. **R/.**
2. let us kneel before the LORD who made us.
   (2.) and we are the people he shep - herds, the flock he guides. **R/.**
3. "Harden not your hearts as at Meribah,
      as in the day of Massah in the des - ert,
   (3.) they tested me though they had seen my works." **R/.**

Tone 8c

B75   Fifth Sunday in Ordinary Time
Psalm 147:1–2, 3–4, 5–6

RESPONSE: *cf. Psalm 147:3a*

Music © 1989, WLP

J. Michael Joncas

A sung Alleluia *may replace this response.*

VERSES

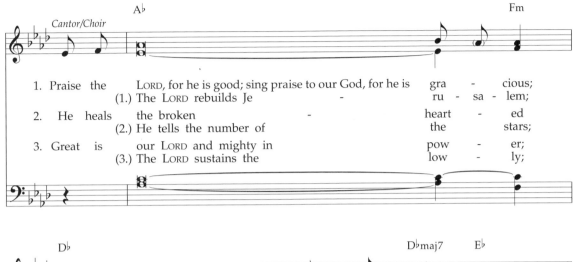

1. Praise the LORD, for he is good; sing praise to our God, for he is gra - cious;
(1.) The LORD rebuilds Je - ru - sa - lem;

2. He heals the broken - heart - ed
(2.) He tells the number of the stars;

3. Great is our LORD and mighty in pow - er;
(3.) The LORD sustains the low - ly;

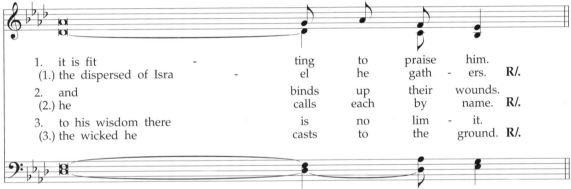

1. it is fit - ting to praise him.
(1.) the dispersed of Isra - el he gath - ers. **R/.**

2. and binds up their wounds.
(2.) he calls each by name. **R/.**

3. to his wisdom there is no lim - it.
(3.) the wicked he casts to the ground. **R/.**

Tone 8G

RESPONSE: *Psalm 32:7*

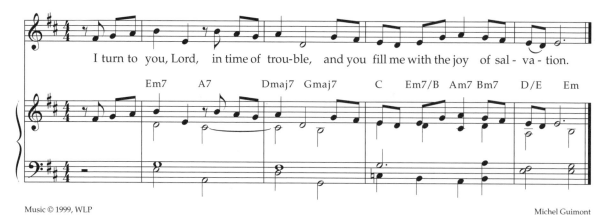

Music © 1999, WLP

Michel Guimont

VERSES

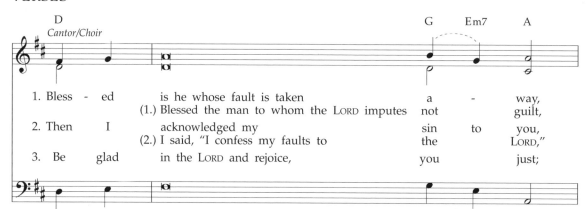

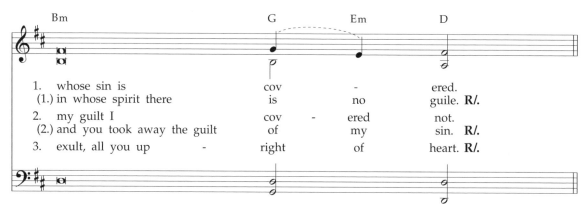

Music © 1984, WLP

James M. Burns

Seventh Sunday in Ordinary Time   B77
Psalm 41:2–3, 4–5, 13–14

RESPONSE: *Psalm 41:5b*

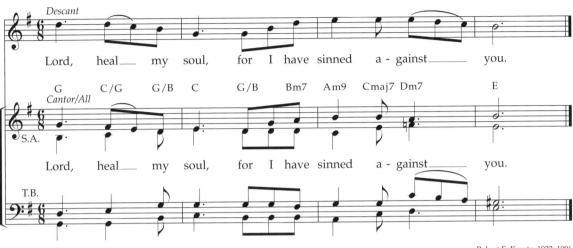

Lord, heal my soul, for I have sinned a-gainst you.

Lord, heal my soul, for I have sinned a-gainst you.

Music © 1972, WLP   Robert E. Kreutz, 1922–1996

VERSES

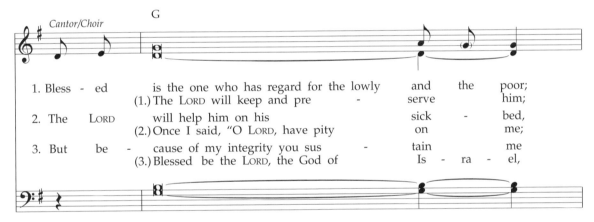

1. Bless - ed   is the one who has regard for the lowly   and   the   poor;
(1.) The LORD will keep and pre   -   serve   him;
2. The   LORD   will help him on his   sick - bed,
(2.) Once I said, "O LORD, have pity   on   me;
3. But   be - cause of my integrity you sus   -   tain   me
(3.) Blessed be the LORD, the God of   Is - ra - el,

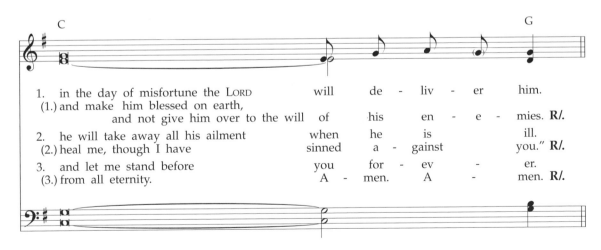

1.   in the day of misfortune the LORD   will   de - liv - er   him.
(1.) and make him blessed on earth,
        and not give him over to the will   of   his   en - e - mies. **R/.**
2.   he will take away all his ailment   when   he   is   ill.
(2.) heal me, though I have   sinned   a - gainst   you." **R/.**
3.   and let me stand before   you   for - ev - er.
(3.) from all eternity.   A - men. A - men. **R/.**

Music © 2000, WLP   Tone 8c

B78 Eighth Sunday in Ordinary Time
Psalm 103:1–2, 3–4, 8, 10, 12–13

LECT. 83

RESPONSE: *Psalm 103:8a*

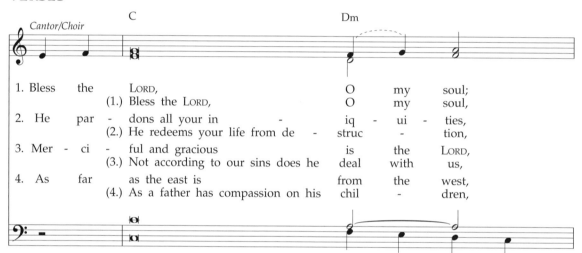

The Lord is kind and mer - ci - ful. mer - ci - ful.

Music © 1982, WLP

Donald J. Reagan

VERSES

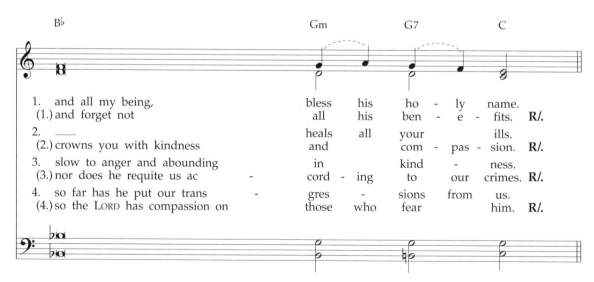

1. Bless the LORD, O my soul;
(1.) Bless the LORD, O my soul,
2. He par - dons all your in - iq - ui - ties,
(2.) He redeems your life from de - struc - tion,
3. Mer - ci - ful and gracious is the LORD,
(3.) Not according to our sins does he deal with us,
4. As far as the east is from the west
(4.) As a father has compassion on his chil - dren,

1. and all my being, bless his ho - ly name.
(1.) and forget not all his ben - e - fits. R/.
2. _____ heals all your ills.
(2.) crowns you with kindness and com - pas - sion. R/.
3. slow to anger and abounding in kind - ness.
(3.) nor does he requite us ac - cord - ing to our crimes. R/.
4. so far has he put our trans - gres - sions from us.
(4.) so the LORD has compassion on those who fear him. R/.

Music © 1984, WLP

Donald J. Reagan

B79 **Ninth Sunday in Ordinary Time**
Psalm 81:3–4, 5–6, 6–8, 10–11

LECT. 86

RESPONSE: *Psalm 81:2a*

Music © 1989, WLP

Donald J. Reagan

VERSES

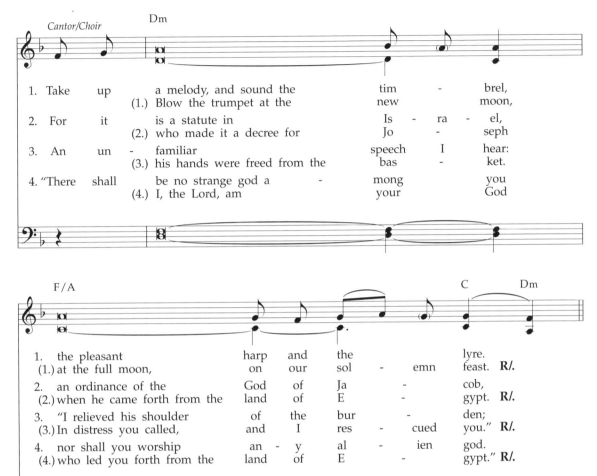

Cantor/Choir

Dm

1. Take up   a melody, and sound the   tim - brel,
(1.) Blow the trumpet at the   new   moon,

2. For it   is a statute in   Is - ra - el,
(2.) who made it a decree for   Jo - seph

3. An un - familiar   speech I hear:
(3.) his hands were freed from the   bas - ket.

4. "There shall   be no strange god a - mong   you
(4.) I, the Lord, am   your   God

F/A   **C** **Dm**

1. the pleasant   harp and the   lyre.
(1.) at the full moon,   on our sol - emn feast. **R/.**

2. an ordinance of the   God of Ja - cob,
(2.) when he came forth from the   land of E - gypt. **R/.**

3. "I relieved his shoulder   of the bur - den;
(3.) In distress you called,   and I res - cued you." **R/.**

4. nor shall you worship   an - y al - ien god.
(4.) who led you forth from the   land of E - gypt." **R/.**

Music © 2000, WLP

Tone 1f, adapt.

B80 Tenth Sunday in Ordinary Time
Psalm 130:1–2, 3–4, 5–6, 7–8

RESPONSE: *Psalm 130:7bc*

With the Lord there is mer-cy and full-ness of re-demp-tion.

Music © 1999, WLP

Michael Bogdan

VERSES

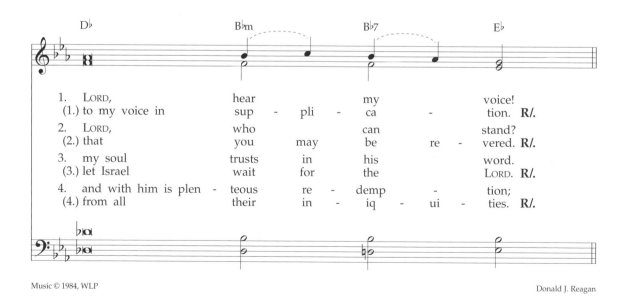

1. Out of the depths I cry to you, O LORD;
(1.) Let your ears be at - ten - tive
2. If you, O LORD, mark in - iq - ui - ties,
(2.) But with you is for - give - ness,
3. I trust in the LORD;
(3.) More than sentinels wait for the dawn,
4. For with the LORD is kind - ness
(4.) and he will redeem Is - ra - el

1. LORD, hear my voice!
(1.) to my voice in sup - pli - ca - tion. **R/.**
2. LORD, who can stand?
(2.) that you may be re - vered. **R/.**
3. my soul trusts in his word.
(3.) let Israel wait for the LORD. **R/.**
4. and with him is plen - teous re - demp - tion;
(4.) from all their in - iq - ui - ties. **R/.**

Music © 1984, WLP

Donald J. Reagan

Eleventh Sunday in Ordinary Time   B81
Psalm 92:2–3, 14, 15-16

RESPONSE: *cf. Psalm 92:2a*

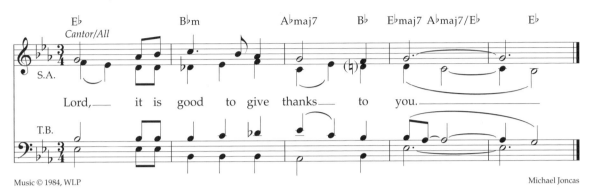

Lord,— it is good to give thanks— to you.—

Music © 1984, WLP

Michael Joncas

VERSES

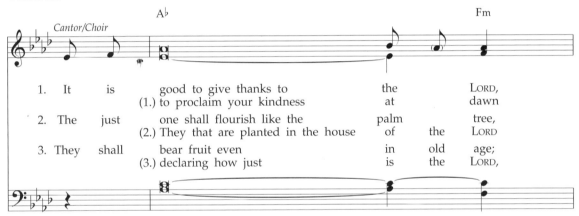

1. It is good to give thanks to the Lord,
(1.) to proclaim your kindness at dawn
2. The just one shall flourish like the palm tree,
(2.) They that are planted in the house of the Lord
3. They shall bear fruit even in old age;
(3.) declaring how just is the Lord,

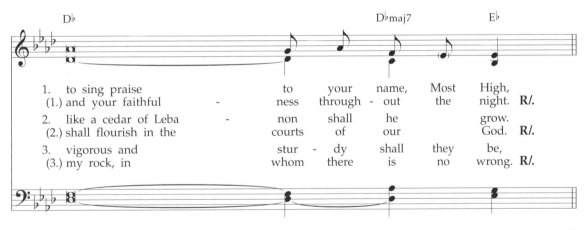

1. to sing praise to your name, Most High,
(1.) and your faithful - ness through - out the night. **R/.**
2. like a cedar of Leba - non shall he grow. **R/.**
(2.) shall flourish in the courts of our God. **R/.**
3. vigorous and stur - dy shall they be,
(3.) my rock, in whom there is no wrong. **R/.**

Music © 2000, WLP

Tone 8G

B82 Twelfth Sunday in Ordinary Time
Psalm 107:23–24, 25–26, 28–29, 30–31

RESPONSE: *Psalm 107:1b*

Music © 1989, WLP

Eugene E. Englert

A sung Alleluia *may replace this response.*

VERSES

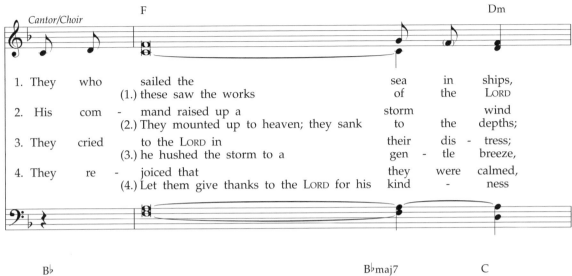

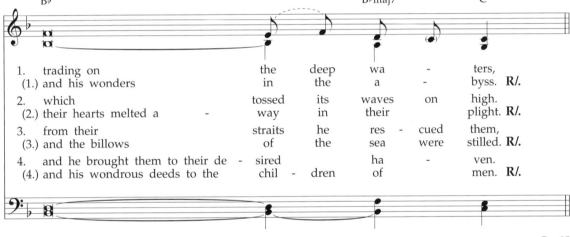

Tone 8G

B83 Thirteenth Sunday in Ordinary Time
Psalm 30:2, 4, 5–6, 11. 12, 13

RESPONSE: *Psalm 30:2a*

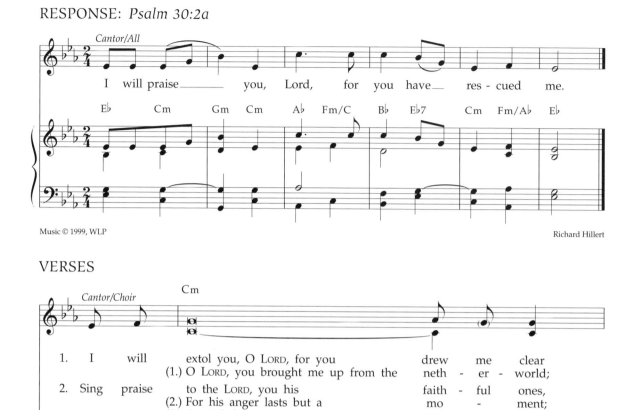

Cantor/All

I will praise you, Lord, for you have res - cued me.

Music © 1999, WLP   Richard Hillert

VERSES

Cantor/Choir

1. I will extol you, O LORD, for you drew me clear
(1.) O LORD, you brought me up from the neth - er - world;
2. Sing praise to the LORD, you his faith - ful ones,
(2.) For his anger lasts but a mo - ment;
(2.) At nightfall, weeping en - ters in,
3. Hear, O LORD, and have pity on me;
(3.) You changed my mourning into danc - ing;

1. and did not let my enemies re - joice o - ver me.
(1.) you preserved me from among those going down in - to the pit. **R/.**
2. and give thanks to his ho - ly name.
(2.) a life - time, his good will.
(2.) but with the dawn, re - joic - ing. **R/.**
3. O LORD, be my help - er.
(3.) O LORD, my God, forever will I give you thanks. **R/.**

Music © 1981, WLP   Tone 1f, adapt.

Fourteenth Sunday in Ordinary Time B84
Psalm 123:1–2, 2, 3–4

RESPONSE: *Psalm 123:2cd*

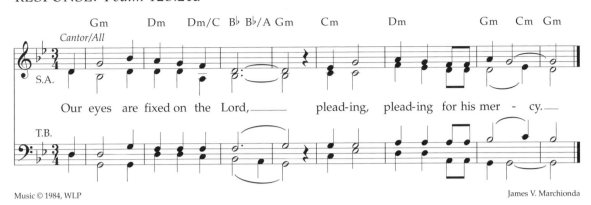

Our eyes are fixed on the Lord,⎯ plead-ing, plead-ing for his mer - cy.⎯

James V. Marchionda

VERSES

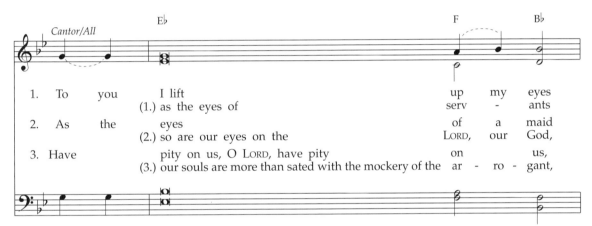

1. To you I lift up my eyes
   (1.) as the eyes of serv - ants
2. As the eyes of a maid
   (2.) so are our eyes on the LORD, our God,
3. Have pity on us, O LORD, have pity on us,
   (3.) our souls are more than sated with the mockery of the ar - ro - gant,

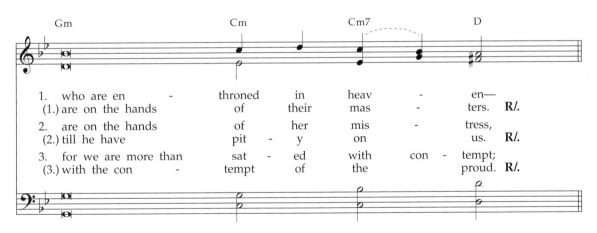

1. who are en - throned in heav - en— R/.
   (1.) are on the hands of their mas - ters. R/.
2. are on the hands of her mis - tress, R/.
   (2.) till he have pit - y on us. R/.
3. for we are more than sat - ed with con - tempt; R/.
   (3.) with the con - tempt of the proud. R/.

James V. Marchionda

B85 Fifteenth Sunday in Ordinary Time
Psalm 85:9–10, 11–12, 13–14

RESPONSE: *Psalm 85:8*

Music © 1999, WLP

Paul M. French

VERSES

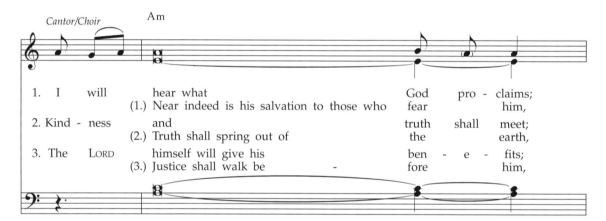

1. I will hear what God pro-claims;
(1.) Near indeed is his salvation to those who fear him,
2. Kind-ness and truth shall meet;
(2.) Truth shall spring out of the earth,
3. The LORD himself will give his ben-e-fits;
(3.) Justice shall walk be-fore him,

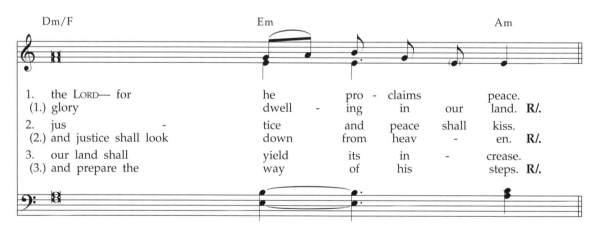

1. the LORD— for he pro-claims peace.
(1.) glory dwell-ing in our land. **R/.**
2. jus-tice and peace shall kiss.
(2.) and justice shall look down from heav-en. **R/.**
3. our land shall yield its in-crease.
(3.) and prepare the way of his steps. **R/.**

Music © 2000, WLP

Tone 4A, adapt.

Sixteenth Sunday in Ordinary Time B86
Psalm 23:1–2, 3–4, 5, 6

RESPONSE: *Psalm 23:1*

The Lord is my shep - herd; there is noth - ing I shall want.

Music © 1970, WLP

Angelo A. della Picca

VERSES

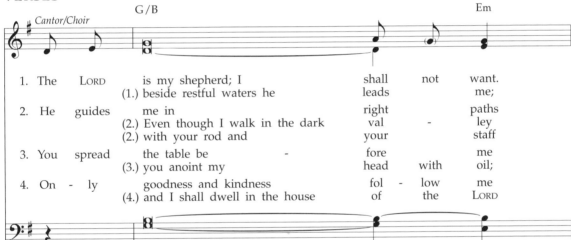

Cantor/Choir

1. The LORD is my shepherd; I shall not want.
(1.) beside restful waters he leads me;
2. He guides me in right paths
(2.) Even though I walk in the dark val - ley
(2.) with your rod and your staff
3. You spread the table be - fore me
(3.) you anoint my head with oil;
4. On - ly goodness and kindness fol - low me
(4.) and I shall dwell in the house of the LORD

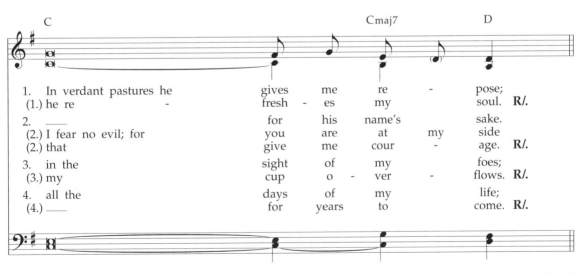

1. In verdant pastures he gives me re - pose;
(1.) he re - fresh - es my soul. **R/.**
2. ___ for his name's sake.
(2.) I fear no evil; for you are at my side
(2.) that give me cour - age. **R/.**
3. in the sight of my foes;
(3.) my cup o - ver - flows. **R/.**
4. all the days of my life;
(4.) ___ for years to come. **R/.**

Music © 2000, WLP

Tone 8G

Psalm 145:10-11, 15–16, 17–18

RESPONSE: *cf. Psalm 145:16*

The hand of the Lord feeds us; he an-swers all our needs.

Music © 1993, 1997, WLP

Ed Bolduc

VERSES

1. Let all your works give you thanks, O LORD,
(1.) Let them discourse of the glory of your king - dom
2. The eyes of all look hopefully to you,
(2.) you open your hand
3. The LORD is just in all his ways
(3.) The LORD is near to all who call up - on him,

1. and let your faith - ful ones bless you.
(1.) and speak of your might. **R/.**
2. and you give them their food in due sea - son;
(2.) and satisfy the desire of every liv - ing thing. **R/.**
3. and holy in all his works.
(3.) to all who call upon him in truth. **R/.**

Music © 1984, WLP

Howard L. Hughes

Eighteenth Sunday in Ordinary Time   B88
Psalm 78:3–4, 23–24, 25, 54

RESPONSE: *Psalm 78:24b*

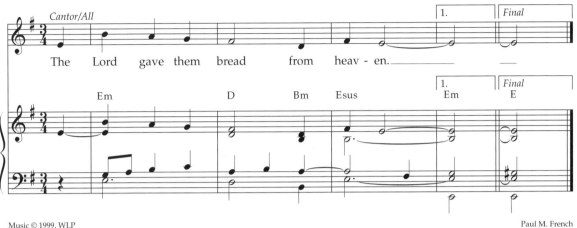

The Lord gave them bread from heav-en.

Paul M. French

VERSES

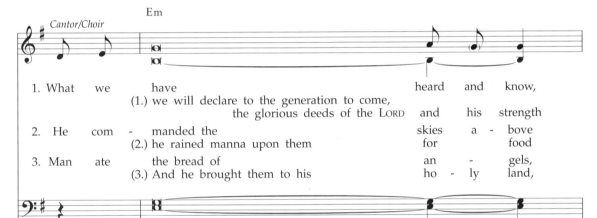

1. What we have heard and know,
(1.) we will declare to the generation to come,
    the glorious deeds of the LORD and his strength
2. He com - manded the skies a - bove
(2.) he rained manna upon them for food
3. Man ate the bread of an - gels,
(3.) And he brought them to his ho - ly land,

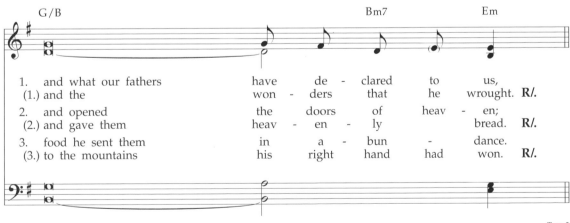

1. and what our fathers have de - clared to us,
(1.) and the won - ders that he wrought. **R/.**
2. and opened the doors of heav - en;
(2.) and gave them heav - en - ly bread. **R/.**
3. food he sent them in a - bun - dance.
(3.) to the mountains his right hand had won. **R/.**

Tone 2

B89 Nineteenth Sunday in Ordinary Time
Psalm 34:2–3, 4–5, 6–7, 8–9

RESPONSE: *Psalm 34:9a*

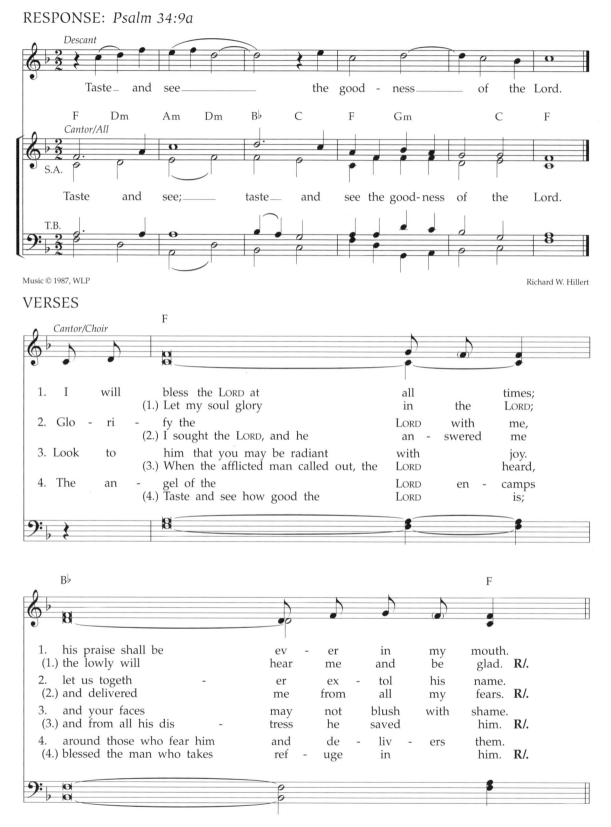

Music © 1987, WLP

Richard W. Hillert

VERSES

1. I will bless the LORD at all times;
   (1.) Let my soul glory in the LORD;
2. Glo - ri - fy the LORD with me,
   (2.) I sought the LORD, and he an - swered me
3. Look to him that you may be radiant with joy.
   (3.) When the afflicted man called out, the LORD heard,
4. The an - gel of the LORD en - camps
   (4.) Taste and see how good the LORD is;

1. his praise shall be ev - er in my mouth.
   (1.) the lowly will hear me and be glad. **R/.**
2. let us togeth - er ex - tol his name.
   (2.) and delivered me from all my fears. **R/.**
3. and your faces may not blush with shame.
   (3.) and from all his dis - tress he saved him. **R/.**
4. around those who fear him and de - liv - ers them.
   (4.) blessed the man who takes ref - uge in him. **R/.**

Music © 2000, WLP

Tone 8c

B90 Twentieth Sunday in Ordinary Time
Psalm 34:2–3, 4–5, 6–7

RESPONSE: *Psalm 34:9a*

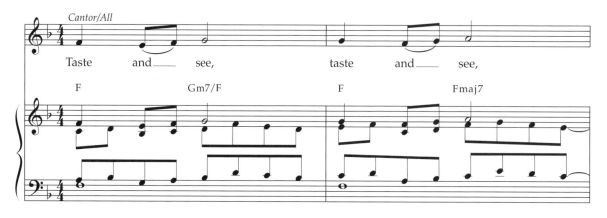

Alan J. Hommerding

VERSES

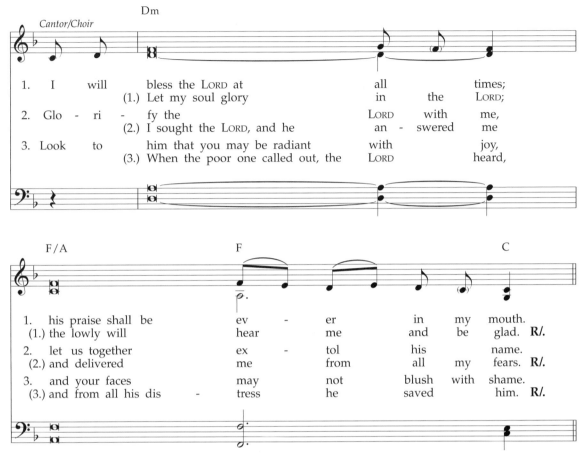

1. I will bless the Lord at all times;
(1.) Let my soul glory in the Lord;
2. Glo - ri - fy the Lord with me,
(2.) I sought the Lord, and he an - swered me
3. Look to him that you may be radiant with joy,
(3.) When the poor one called out, the Lord heard,

1. his praise shall be ev - er in my mouth.
(1.) the lowly will hear me and be glad. **R/.**
2. let us together ex - tol his name.
(2.) and delivered me from all my fears. **R/.**
3. and your faces may not blush with shame.
(3.) and from all his dis - tress he saved him. **R/.**

Tone 3g, adapt.

B91 Twenty-first Sunday in Ordinary Time
Psalm 34:2–3, 16–17, 18–19, 20–21

RESPONSE: *Psalm 34:9a*

Music © 1987, WLP

Richard W. Hillert

VERSES

1. I will bless the Lord at all times;
(1.) Let my soul glory in the Lord;
2. The Lord has eyes for the just,
(2.) The Lord confronts the evil - do - ers,
3. When the just cry out, the Lord hears them,
(3.) The Lord is close to the broken - heart - ed;
4. Man - y are the troubles of the just one,
(4.) he watches over all his bones;

1. his praise shall be ev - er in my mouth.
(1.) the lowly will hear me and be glad. **R/.**
2. and ears for their cry.
(2.) to destroy remembrance of them from the earth. **R/.**
3. and from all their dis - tress he res - cues them.
(3.) and those who are crushed in spir - it he saves. **R/.**
4. but out of them all the Lord de - liv - ers him;
(4.) not one of them shall be bro - ken. **R/.**

Music © 2000, WLP

Tone 8c

Twenty-second Sunday in Ordinary Time   B92
Psalm 15:2–3, 3–4, 4–5

RESPONSE: *Psalm 15:1a*

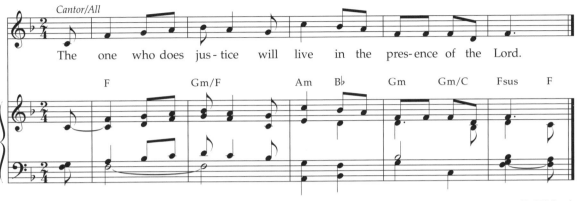

Cantor/All

The one who does jus-tice will live in the pres-ence of the Lord.

Music © 1999, WLP

Paul M. French

VERSES

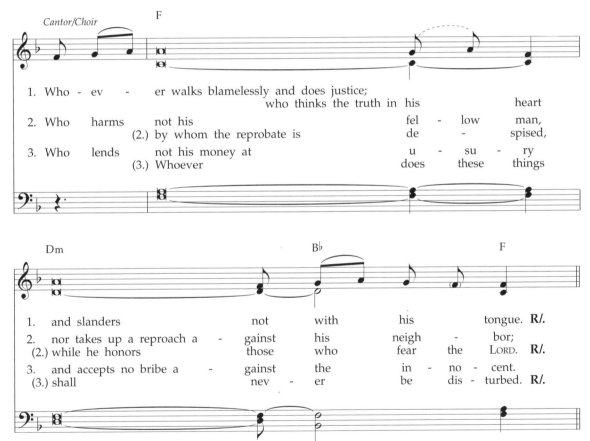

Cantor/Choir

1. Who - ev - er walks blamelessly and does justice;
   who thinks the truth in his heart
2. Who harms not his fel - low man,
   (2.) by whom the reprobate is de - spised,
3. Who lends not his money at u - su - ry
   (3.) Whoever does these things

1. and slanders not with his tongue. **R/.**
2. nor takes up a reproach a - gainst his neigh - bor;
   (2.) while he honors those who fear the LORD. **R/.**
3. and accepts no bribe a - gainst the in - no - cent.
   (3.) shall nev - er be dis - turbed. **R/.**

Music © 2000, WLP

Tone 6

RESPONSE: *Psalm 146:1b*

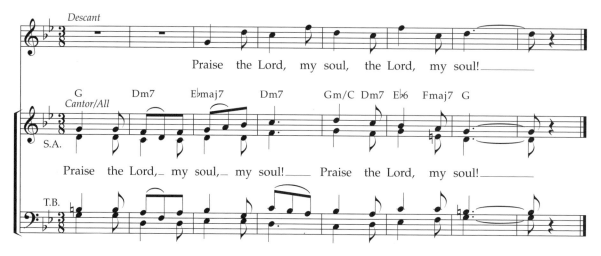

Praise the Lord, my soul, the Lord, my soul!

Praise the Lord, my soul, my soul! Praise the Lord, my soul!

Paul Lisicky

A sung Alleluia *may replace this response.*

VERSES

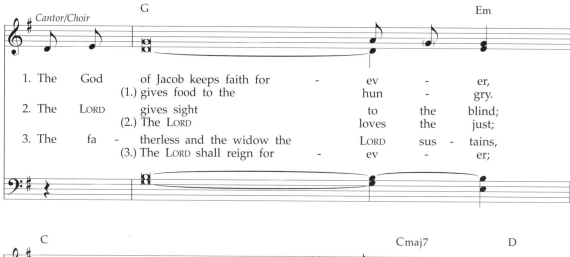

1. The God of Jacob keeps faith for - ev - er,
 (1.) gives food to the hun - gry.
2. The LORD gives sight to the blind;
 (2.) The LORD loves the just;
3. The fa - therless and the widow the LORD sus - tains,
 (3.) The LORD shall reign for - ev - er;

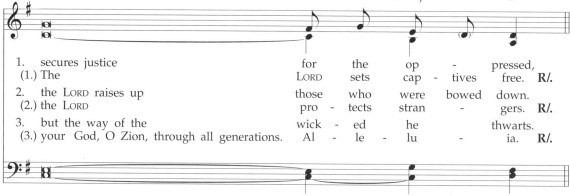

1. secures justice for the op - pressed, **R/.**
 (1.) The LORD sets cap - tives free. **R/.**
2. the LORD raises up those who were bowed down.
 (2.) the LORD pro - tects stran - gers. **R/.**
3. but the way of the wick - ed he thwarts.
 (3.) your God, O Zion, through all generations. Al - le - lu - ia. **R/.**

Tone 8G

B94 Twenty-fourth Sunday in Ordinary Time

B94 **Twenty-fourth Sunday in Ordinary Time**
Psalm 116:1–2, 3–4, 5–6, 8–9

B94   Twenty-fourth Sunday in Ordinary Time
Psalm 116:1–2, 3–4, 5–6, 8–9

Lect. 131

RESPONSE: *Psalm 116:9*

Music © 1994, WLP

Howard Hughes

A sung Alleluia *may replace this response.*

VERSES

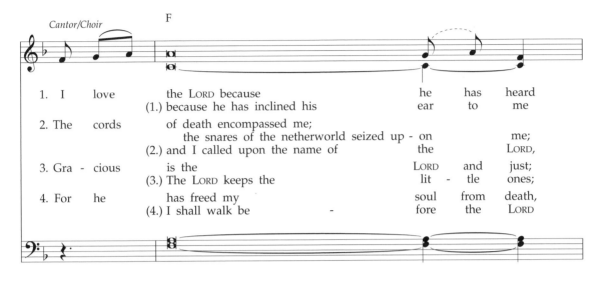

Tone 6

B95 Twenty-fifth Sunday in Ordinary Time
Psalm 54:3-4, 5, 6–8

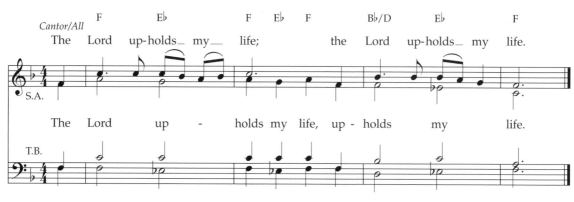

RESPONSE: *Psalm 54:6b*

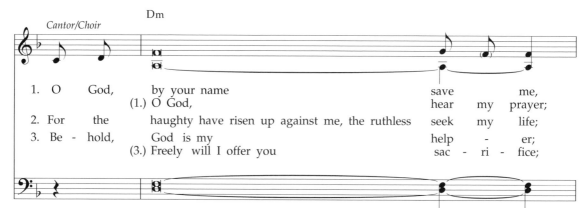

Music © 1989, WLP

Michael Joncas

VERSES

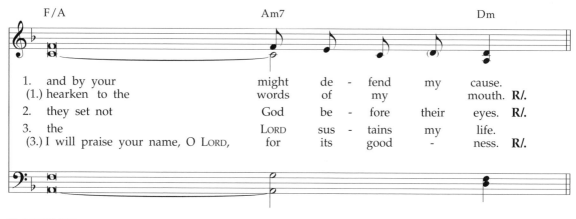

Music © 2000, WLP

Tone 2

Twenty-sixth Sunday in Ordinary Time   B96
Psalm 19:8, 10, 12–13, 14

RESPONSE: *Psalm 19:9a*

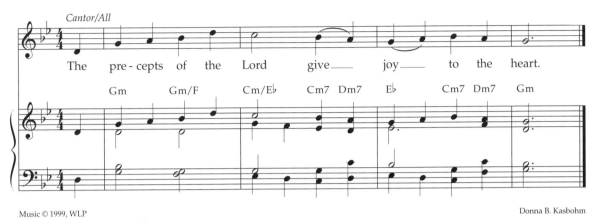

The pre-cepts of the Lord give joy to the heart.

Music © 1999, WLP

Donna B. Kasbohm

VERSES

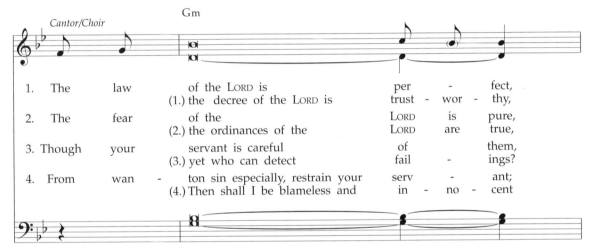

1. The law of the LORD is per - fect,
(1.) the decree of the LORD is trust - wor - thy,
2. The fear of the LORD is pure,
(2.) the ordinances of the LORD are true,
3. Though your servant is careful of them,
(3.) yet who can detect fail - ings?
4. From wan - ton sin especially, restrain your serv - ant;
(4.) Then shall I be blameless and in - no - cent

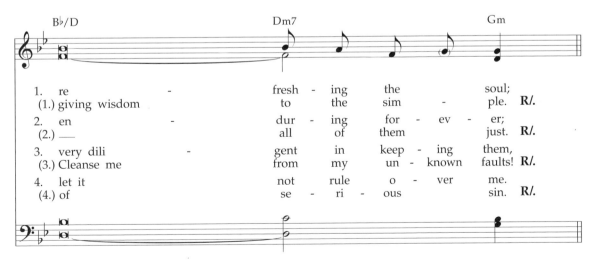

1. re - fresh - ing the soul; R/.
(1.) giving wisdom to the sim - ple. R/.
2. en - dur - ing for - ev - er;
(2.) — all of them just. R/.
3. very dili - gent in keep - ing them,
(3.) Cleanse me from my un - known faults! R/.
4. let it not rule o - ver me.
(4.) of se - ri - ous sin. R/.

Music © 2000, WLP

Tone 2

B97 Twenty-seventh Sunday in Ordinary Time
Psalm 128:1–2, 3, 4–5, 6

RESPONSE: *cf. Psalm 128:5*

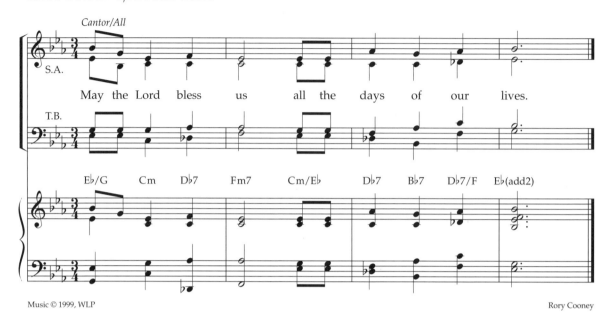

May the Lord bless us all the days of our lives.

Music © 1999, WLP

Rory Cooney

VERSES

1. Bless - ed are you who fear the LORD,
(1.) For you shall eat the fruit of your hand - i - work;
2. Your wife shall be like a fruit - ful vine
(2.) your children like ol - ive plants
3. Be - hold, thus is the man blessed
(3.) The LORD bless you from Zi - on:
4. May you see your children's chil - dren.

1. who walk in his ways!
(1.) blessed shall you be, and fa - vored. **R/.**
2. in the re - cesses of your home; **R/.**
(2.) a - round your ta - ble. **R/.**
3. ___ who fears the LORD. **R/.**
(3.) may you see the prosperity of Jerusalem all the days of your life. **R/.**
4. Peace be up - on Is - ra - el! **R/.**

Tone 6

B98 Twenty-eighth Sunday in Ordinary Time
Psalm 90:12–13, 14–15, 16–17

RESPONSE: *Psalm 90:14*

Descant

Fill us with your love, we will sing for joy!

Cantor/All

S.A.

Fill us with your love, O Lord, and we will sing for joy!

T.B.

D   G(add2)   Em7   G/A   A   D

Ed Bolduc

VERSES

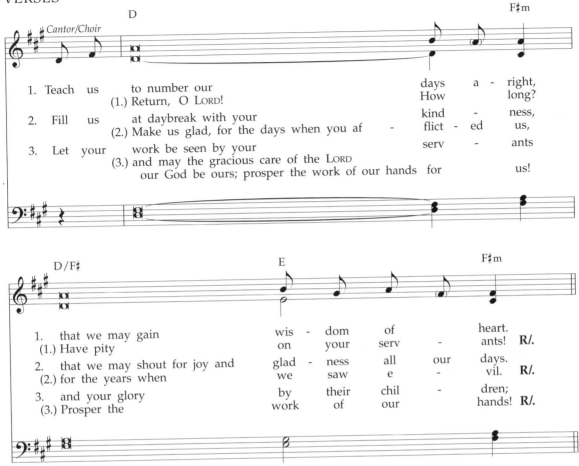

1. Teach us to number our days a - right,
(1.) Return, O LORD! How long?

2. Fill us at daybreak with your kind - ness,
(2.) Make us glad, for the days when you af - flict - ed us,

3. Let your work be seen by your serv - ants
(3.) and may the gracious care of the LORD our God be ours; prosper the work of our hands for us!

1. that we may gain wis - dom of heart.
(1.) Have pity on your serv - ants! **R/.**

2. that we may shout for joy and glad - ness all our days.
(2.) for the years when we saw e - vil. **R/.**

3. and your glory by their chil - dren;
(3.) Prosper the work of our hands! **R/.**

Music © 2000, WLP

Tone 5

B99 Twenty-ninth Sunday in Ordinary Time
Psalm 33:4–5, 18–19, 20, 22

RESPONSE: *Psalm 33:22*

Music © 1987, WLP

Howard L. Hughes

VERSES

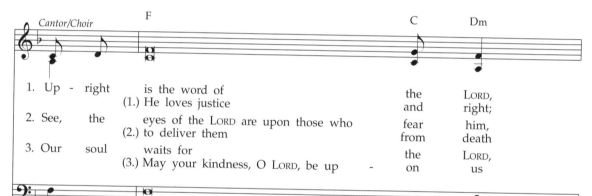

1. Up - right   is the word of   the   LORD,
(1.) He loves justice   and   right;
2. See,   the   eyes of the LORD are upon those who   fear   him,
(2.) to deliver them   from   death
3. Our   soul   waits for   the   LORD,
(3.) May your kindness, O LORD, be up   -   on   us

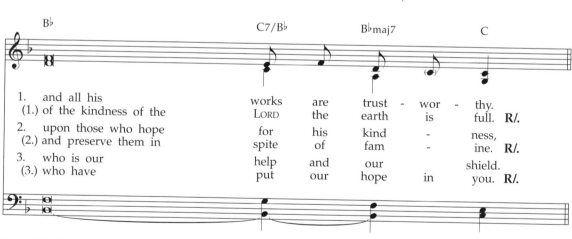

1.   and all his   works   are   trust - wor - thy.
(1.) of the kindness of the   LORD   the   earth   is   full. **R/.**
2.   upon those who hope   for   his   kind   -   ness,
(2.) and preserve them in   spite   of   fam   -   ine. **R/.**
3.   who is our   help   and   our   shield.
(3.) who have   put   our   hope   in   you. **R/.**

Music © 1972, WLP

Tone 8G

Thirtieth Sunday in Ordinary Time B100
Psalm 126:1–2, 2–3, 4–5, 6

RESPONSE: *Psalm 126:3*

Music © 1988, WLP

James V. Marchionda

VERSES

Music © 2000, WLP

Tone 8G

B101 Thirty-first Sunday in Ordinary Time
Psalm 18:2–3, 3–4, 47, 51

RESPONSE: *Psalm 18:2*

Descant (after vss. 2 and 3)

I love_____ you, Lord,_____ I love_____ you._____

Cantor/All

I love_____ you, Lord, I love you, Lord, my strength._____

G(no 3rd) Am7 Cmaj7 Dsus D7 G D/C G/B Am7 D(no 3rd)

Ped.

Music © 1995, WLP

Richard T. Proulx

VERSES

Cantor/Choir

D   F♯m

1. I love you, O LORD,   my strength,
2. My God, my rock of   ref - uge,
   (2.) Praised be the LORD,   I ex - claim,
3. The LORD lives! And blessed be   my rock!
   (3.) you who gave great victories   to your king

D/F♯   E   F♯m

1. O LORD, my rock, my fortress,   my de - liv - er - er. **R/.**
2. my shield, the horn of my sal - va - tion, my strong - hold!
   (2.) and I am safe from my en - e - mies. **R/.**
3. Extolled be God my sav - ior.
   (3.) and showed kindness to your a - noint - ed. **R/.**

Music © 2000, WLP

Tone 5

Thirty-second Sunday in Ordinary Time B102
Psalm 146:7, 8–9, 9–10

RESPONSE: *Psalm 146:1b*

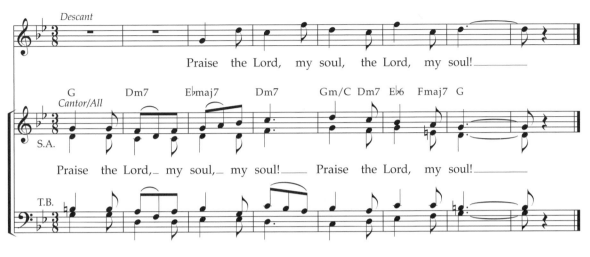

Music © 1988, WLP

Paul Lisicky

A sung Alleluia *may replace this response.*

VERSES

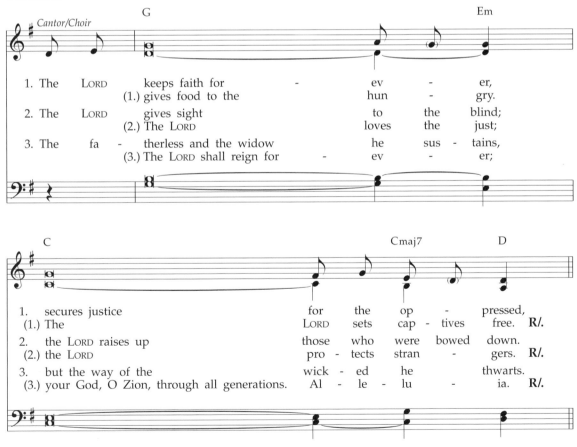

Music © 2000, WLP

Tone 8G

B103 Thirty-third Sunday in Ordinary Time
Psalm 16:5, 8, 9–10, 11

RESPONSE: *Psalm 16:1*

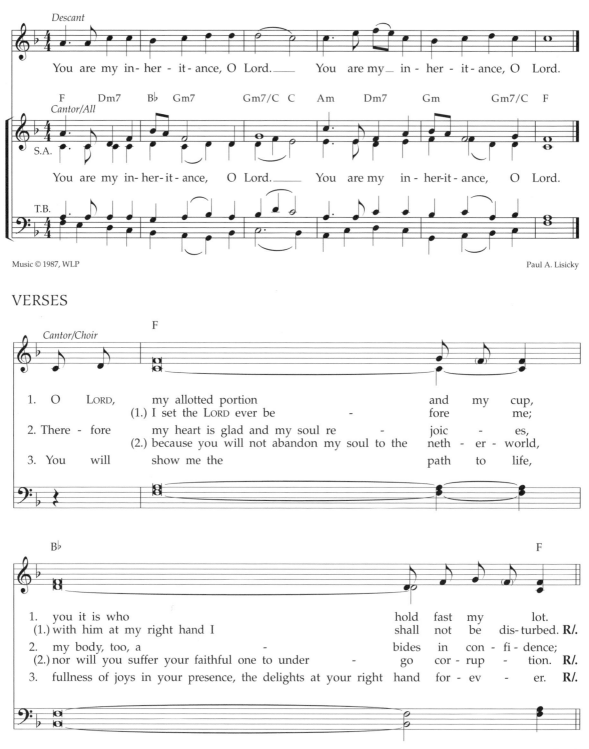

You are my in-her-it-ance, O Lord. You are my in-her-it-ance, O Lord.

You are my in-her-it-ance, O Lord. You are my in-her-it-ance, O Lord.

Music © 1987, WLP

Paul A. Lisicky

VERSES

1. O Lord, my allotted portion and my cup,
(1.) I set the Lord ever be - fore me;
2. There - fore my heart is glad and my soul re - joic - es,
(2.) because you will not abandon my soul to the neth - er - world,
3. You will show me the path to life,

1. you it is who hold fast my lot.
(1.) with him at my right hand I shall not be dis-turbed. R/.
2. my body, too, a - bides in con - fi - dence;
(2.) nor will you suffer your faithful one to under - go cor-rup - tion. R/.
3. fullness of joys in your presence, the delights at your right hand for - ev - er. R/.

Music © 2000, WLP

Tone 8c

The Solemnity of Our Lord Jesus Christ the King   B104
Psalm 93:1, 1–2, 5

RESPONSE: *Psalm 93:1a*

Music © 1970, WLP

J. Gerald Phillips

VERSES

1. The LORD is king, in splen-dor robed;
2. And he has made the world firm,
(2.) Your throne stands firm from of old;
3. Your de-crees are worthy of trust in-deed;

1. robed is the LORD and girt a-bout with strength. **R/.**
2. not to be moved.
(2.) from everlasting you are, O LORD. **R/.**
3. holiness befits your house, O LORD, for length of days. **R/.**

Music © 2000, WLP

Tone 8G

B105 The Presentation of the Lord
Psalm 24:7, 8, 9, 10

RESPONSE: *Psalm 24:8*

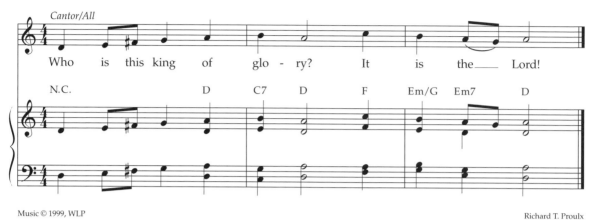

Cantor/All

Who is this king of glo - ry? It is the ____ Lord!

N.C.   D   C7   D   F   Em/G   Em7   D

Music © 1999, WLP

Richard T. Proulx

VERSES

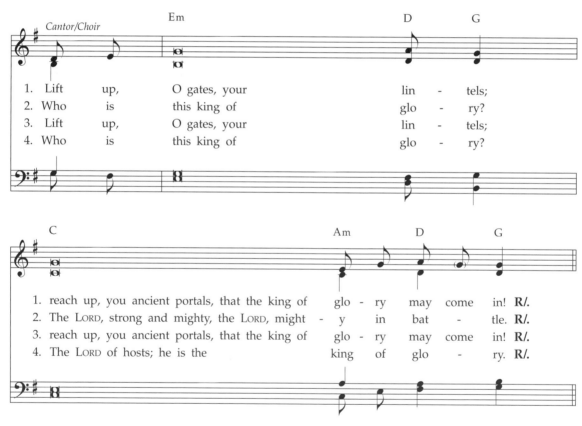

Cantor/Choir

Em   D   G

1. Lift up, O gates, your lin - tels;
2. Who is this king of glo - ry?
3. Lift up, O gates, your lin - tels;
4. Who is this king of glo - ry?

C   Am   D   G

1. reach up, you ancient portals, that the king of glo - ry may come in! **R/.**
2. The LORD, strong and mighty, the LORD, might - y in bat - tle. **R/.**
3. reach up, you ancient portals, that the king of glo - ry may come in! **R/.**
4. The LORD of hosts; he is the king of glo - ry. **R/.**

Music © 1972, WLP

Tone 8c

St. Joseph, Husband of the Blessed Virgin Mary B106
Psalm 89:2–3, 4–5, 27, 29

RESPONSE: *Psalm 89:37*

The son of Da - vid will live for ev - er.

A   E   F♯m7 C♯m   F♯m/A   B7   F♯m/C♯   E

Steven C. Warner

VERSES

Cantor/Choir   E   F♯m

1. The prom - ises of the LORD I will sing for - ev - er;
(1.) for you have said, "My kindness is established for - ev - er";
2. "I have made a covenant with my cho - sen one,
(2.) forever will I confirm your pos - ter - i - ty
3. "He shall say of me, 'You are my fa - ther,
(3.) Forever I will maintain my kindness toward him,

D   Bm   B7   E

1. through all generations my mouth shall pro - claim your faith - ful - ness,
(1.) in heaven you have con - firmed your faith - ful - ness. **R/.**
2. I have sworn to David my serv - ant:
(2.) and establish your throne for all gen - er - a - tions." **R/.**
3. my God, the Rock my sav - ior.'
(3.) and my covenant with him stands firm." **R/.**

Donald J. Reagan

B107 The Annunciation of the Lord
Psalm 40:7–8, 8–9, 10, 11

RESPONSE: *Psalm 40:8a, 9b*

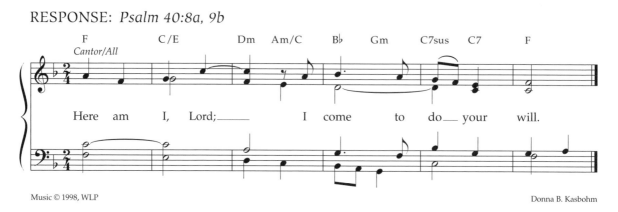

Here am I, Lord;____ I come to do__ your will.

Donna B. Kasbohm

VERSES

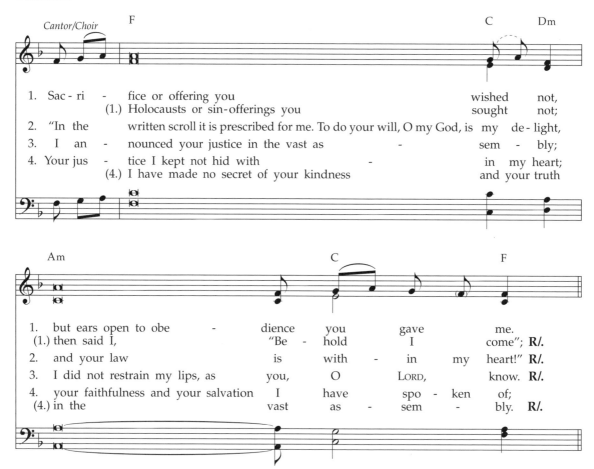

1. Sac - ri - fice or offering you wished not,
  (1.) Holocausts or sin-offerings you sought not;
2. "In the written scroll it is prescribed for me. To do your will, O my God, is my de-light,
3. I an - nounced your justice in the vast as - sem - bly;
4. Your jus - tice I kept not hid with - in my heart;
  (4.) I have made no secret of your kindness and your truth

1. but ears open to obe - dience you gave me.
  (1.) then said I, "Be - hold I come"; **R/.**
2. and your law is with - in my heart!" **R/.**
3. I did not restrain my lips, as you, O LORD, know. **R/.**
4. your faithfulness and your salvation I have spo - ken of;
  (4.) in the vast as - sem - bly. **R/.**

Tone 6

RESPONSE: *Psalm 71:6b*

Since my mother's womb, you have been my strength.

Music © 1999, WLP   Donna Kasbohm

VERSES

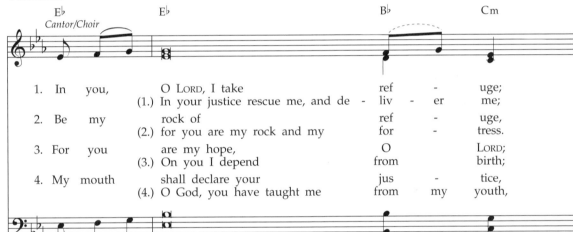

1. In you,   O LORD, I take   ref - uge;
(1.) In your justice rescue me, and de - liv - er me;
2. Be my   rock of   ref - uge,
(2.) for you are my rock and my   for - tress.
3. For you   are my hope,   O   LORD;
(3.) On you I depend   from birth;
4. My mouth   shall declare your   jus - tice,
(4.) O God, you have taught me   from my youth,

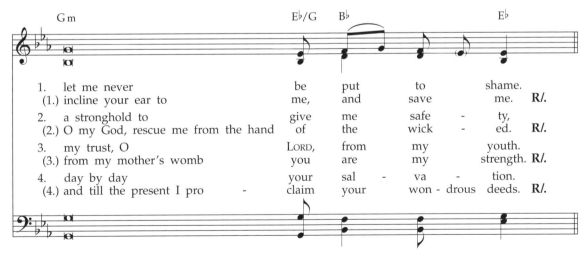

1. let me never   be   put   to   shame. **R/.**
(1.) incline your ear to   me, and save me. **R/.**
2. a stronghold to   give me safe - ty,
(2.) O my God, rescue me from the hand of the wick - ed. **R/.**
3. my trust, O   LORD, from my youth.
(3.) from my mother's womb   you are my strength. **R/.**
4. day by day   your sal - va - tion.
(4.) and till the present I pro - claim your won - drous deeds. **R/.**

Music © 1981, WLP   Tone 6

B109 The Nativity of St. John the Baptist, Mass during the Day
Psalm 139:1–3, 13–14, 14–15

RESPONSE: *Psalm 139:14a*

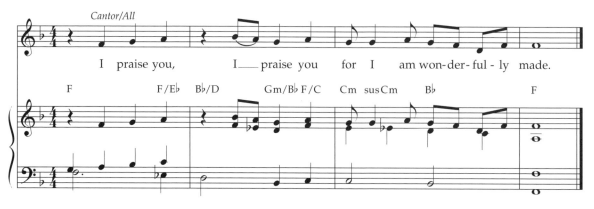

I praise you, I praise you for I am won-der-ful-ly made.

Music © 1999, WLP

Michael Bogdan

VERSES

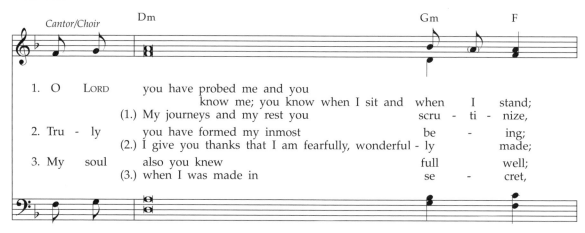

1. O LORD you have probed me and you
     know me; you know when I sit and when I stand;
     (1.) My journeys and my rest you scru - ti - nize,
2. Tru - ly you have formed my inmost be - ing;
     (2.) I give you thanks that I am fearfully, wonderful - ly made;
3. My soul also you knew full well;
     (3.) when I was made in se - cret,

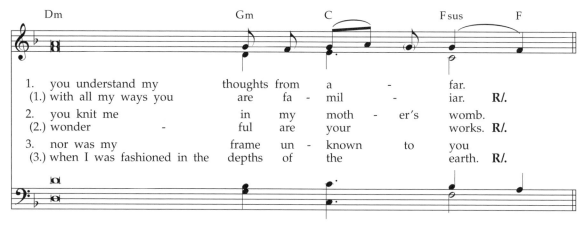

1. you understand my thoughts from a - far.
   (1.) with all my ways you are fa - mil - iar. **R/.**
2. you knit me in my moth - er's womb.
   (2.) wonder - ful are your works. **R/.**
3. nor was my frame un - known to you
   (3.) when I was fashioned in the depths of the earth. **R/.**

Music © 1972, WLP

Tone 1f, adapt.

SS. Peter and Paul, Apostles, at the Vigil Mass   B110
Psalm 19:2–3, 4–5

RESPONSE: *Psalm 19:5a*

Music © 1987, WLP

Michael Ward

VERSES

Music © 1972, WLP

Tone 5

B111 SS. Peter and Paul, Apostles, Mass during the Day Lect. 591
Psalm 34:2–3, 4–5, 6–7, 8–9

RESPONSE: *Psalm 34:5b*

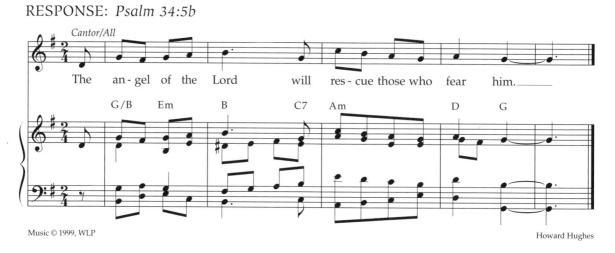

The an-gel of the Lord will res-cue those who fear him.____

Music © 1999, WLP

Howard Hughes

VERSES

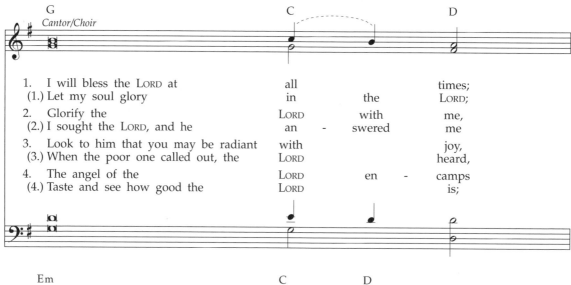

1. I will bless the Lord at all times;
(1.) Let my soul glory in the Lord;

2. Glorify the Lord with me,
(2.) I sought the Lord, and he an - swered me

3. Look to him that you may be radiant with joy,
(3.) When the poor one called out, the Lord heard,

4. The angel of the Lord en - camps
(4.) Taste and see how good the Lord is;

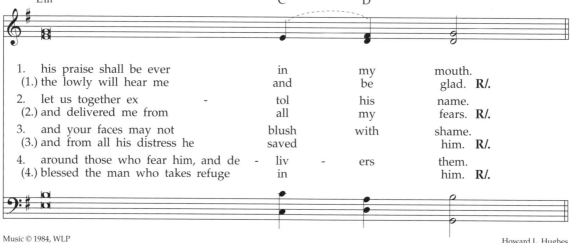

1. his praise shall be ever in my mouth.
(1.) the lowly will hear me and be glad. **R/.**

2. let us together ex - tol his name.
(2.) and delivered me from all my fears. **R/.**

3. and your faces may not blush with shame.
(3.) and from all his distress he saved him. **R/.**

4. around those who fear him, and de - liv - ers them.
(4.) blessed the man who takes refuge in him. **R/.**

Music © 1984, WLP

Howard L. Hughes

The Transfiguration of the Lord B112
Psalm 97:1–2, 5–6, 9

RESPONSE: *Psalm 97:1a, 9a*

Music © 1971, WLP

H. Hamilton Smith

VERSES

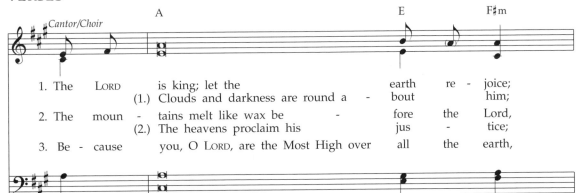

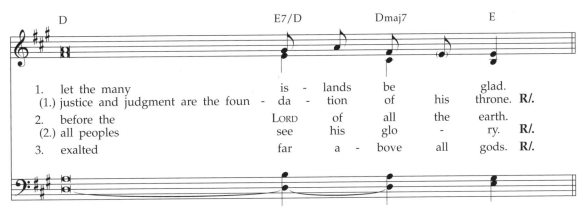

Music © 1971, WLP

Tone 8G

B113 The Assumption of the Blessed Virgin Mary, at the Vigil Mass

Psalm 132:6–7, 9–10, 13–14

RESPONSE: *Psalm 132:8*

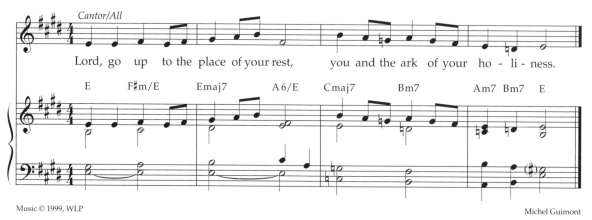

Lord, go up to the place of your rest, you and the ark of your ho-li-ness.

Music © 1999, WLP

Michel Guimont

VERSES

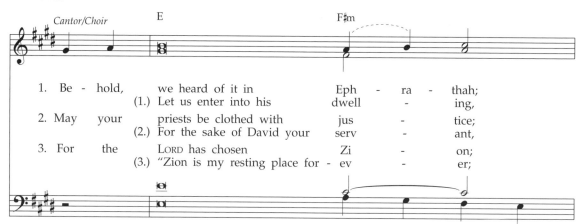

1. Be - hold, we heard of it in Eph - ra - thah;
(1.) Let us enter into his dwell - ing,
2. May your priests be clothed with jus - tice;
(2.) For the sake of David your serv - ant,
3. For the LORD has chosen Zi - on;
(3.) "Zion is my resting place for - ev - er;

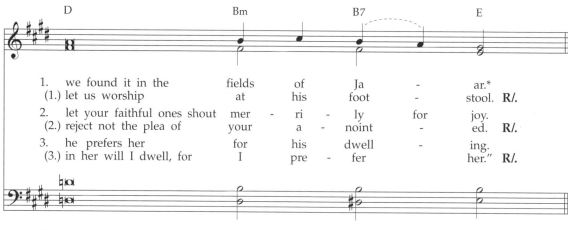

1. we found it in the fields of Ja - ar.*
(1.) let us worship at his foot - stool. **R/.**
2. let your faithful ones shout mer - ri - ly for joy.
(2.) reject not the plea of your a - noint - ed. **R/.**
3. he prefers her for his dwell - ing.
(3.) in her will I dwell, for I pre - fer her." **R/.**

Music © 1984, WLP

Donald J. Reagan

* pronounced "ya-AR"

The Assumption of the Blessed Virgin Mary, B114
Mass during the Day
Psalm 45:10, 11, 12, 16

RESPONSE: *Psalm 45:10bc*

The queen stands at your right hand, ar - rayed in gold.

G   D/C   G/B   B♭maj7   C   D

Music © 1993, WLP

Ed Bolduc

VERSES

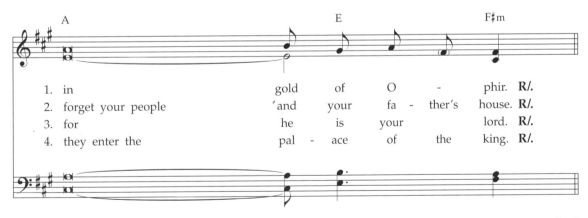

Cantor/Choir

A   E   F♯m

1. The queen takes her place at your right hand
2. Hear, O daughter, and see; turn your ear,
3. So shall the king desire your beau - ty;
4. They are borne in with gladness and joy;

A   E   F♯m

1. in gold of O - phir. **R/.**
2. forget your people 'and your fa - ther's house. **R/.**
3. for he is your lord. **R/.**
4. they enter the pal - ace of the king. **R/.**

Music © 1972, WLP

Tone 5

B115 The Exaltation of the Holy Cross
Psalm 78:1–2, 34–35, 36–37, 38

RESPONSE: *cf. Psalm 78:7*

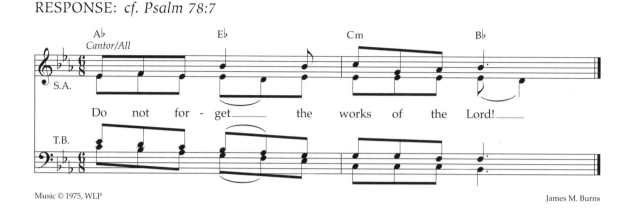

Music © 1975, WLP   James M. Burns

VERSES

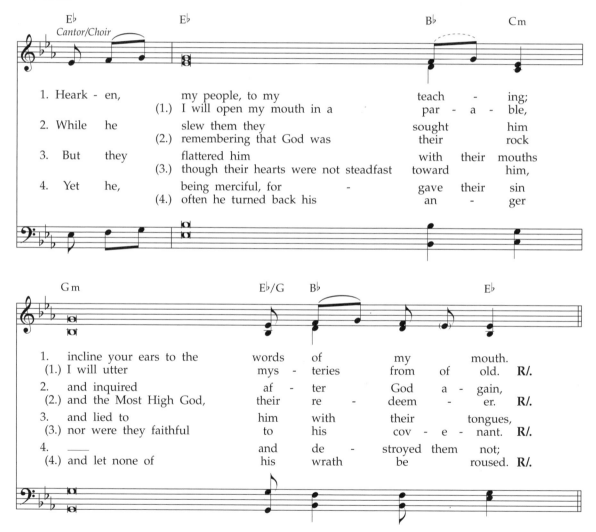

Music © 1981, WLP   Tone 6

All Saints B116
Psalm 24:1–2, 3–4, 5–6

RESPONSE: *cf. Psalm 24:6*

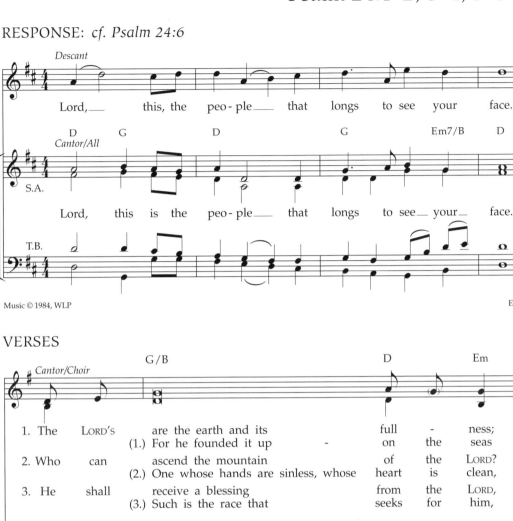

Lord, this, the peo-ple that longs to see your face.

Lord, this is the peo-ple that longs to see your face.

Music © 1984, WLP   Eugene E. Englert

VERSES

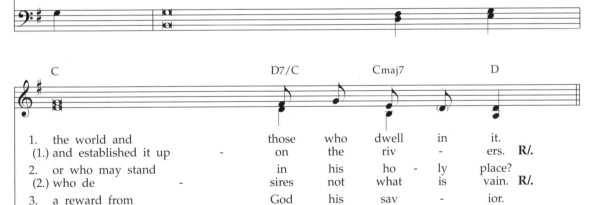

1. The LORD'S are the earth and its full - ness;
(1.) For he founded it up - on the seas
2. Who can ascend the mountain of the LORD?
(2.) One whose hands are sinless, whose heart is clean,
3. He shall receive a blessing from the LORD,
(3.) Such is the race that seeks for him,

1. the world and those who dwell in it.
(1.) and established it up - on the riv - ers. **R/.**
2. or who may stand in his ho - ly place?
(2.) who de - sires not what is vain. **R/.**
3. a reward from God his sav - ior.
(3.) that seeks the face of the God of Ja - cob. **R/.**

Music © 1982, WLP   Tone 8G

B117 The Dedication of the Lateran Basilica
Psalm 46:2–3, 5–6, 8–9

RESPONSE: *Psalm 46:5*

The wa-ters of the riv - er glad - den the cit - y of God,

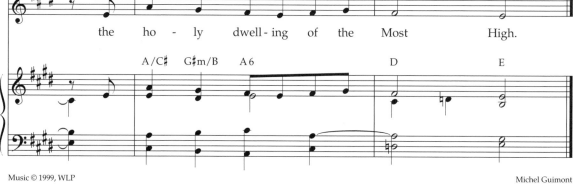

the ho - ly dwell - ing of the Most High.

Michel Guimont

VERSES

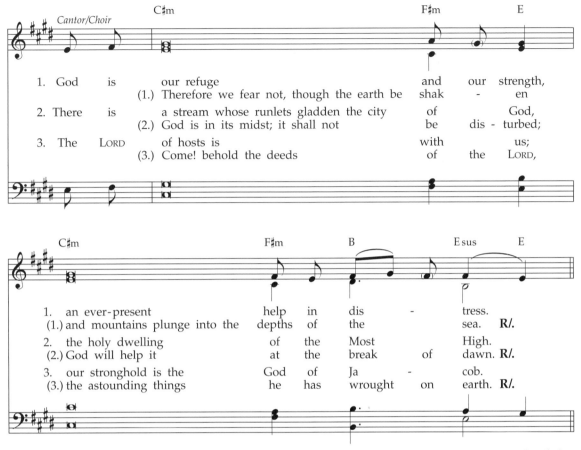

1. God is our refuge and our strength,
(1.) Therefore we fear not, though the earth be shak - en

2. There is a stream whose runlets gladden the city of God,
(2.) God is in its midst; it shall not be dis - turbed;

3. The LORD of hosts is with us;
(3.) Come! behold the deeds of the LORD,

1. an ever-present help in dis - tress. **R/.**
(1.) and mountains plunge into the depths of the sea. **R/.**

2. the holy dwelling of the Most High.
(2.) God will help it at the break of dawn. **R/.**

3. our stronghold is the God of Ja - cob.
(3.) the astounding things he has wrought on earth. **R/.**

Music © 1981, WLP
Tone 1f, adapt.

B118 The Immaculate Conception
of the Blessed Virgin Mary
Psalm 98:1, 2–3, 3–4

RESPONSE: *Psalm 98:1a*

Sing to the Lord a new song, for he has done mar-vel-ous deeds.

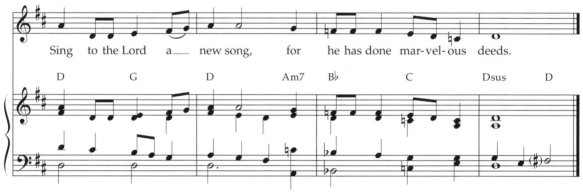

Sing to the Lord a new song, for he has done mar-vel-ous deeds.

Michael Bedford

VERSES

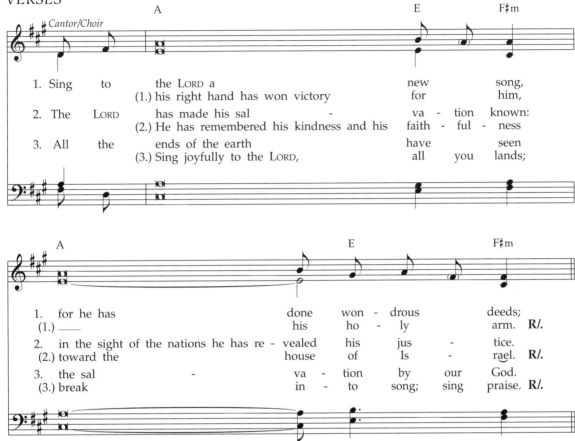

1. Sing to the LORD a new song,
(1.) his right hand has won victory for him,
2. The LORD has made his sal - va - tion known:
(2.) He has remembered his kindness and his faith - ful - ness
3. All the ends of the earth have seen
(3.) Sing joyfully to the LORD, all you lands;

1. for he has done won - drous deeds;
(1.) ——— his ho - ly arm. **R/.**
2. in the sight of the nations he has re - vealed his jus - tice.
(2.) toward the house of Is - rael. **R/.**
3. the sal - va - tion by our God.
(3.) break in - to song; sing praise. **R/.**

Tone 5

B119 Our Lady of Guadalupe
Revised
Judith 13:18bcde, 19

RESPONSE: *Judith 15:9d*

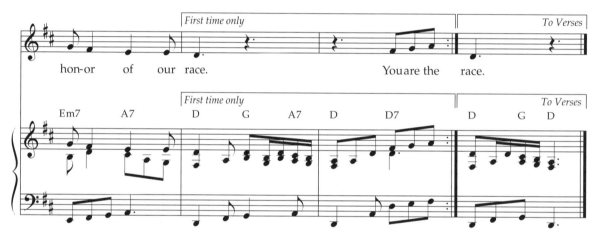

Music © 2002, WLP

Peter M. Kolar

VERSES

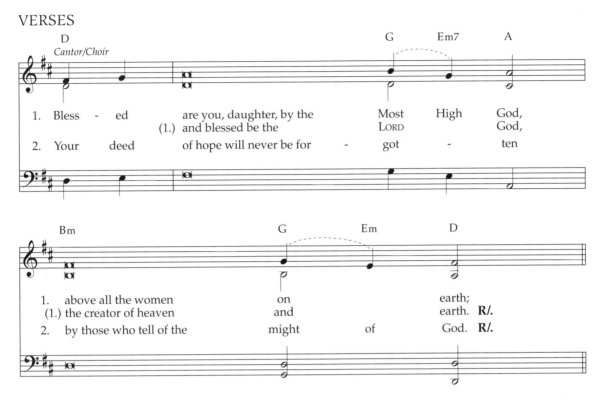

1. Bless - ed are you, daughter, by the Most High God,
(1.) and blessed be the LORD God,
2. Your deed of hope will never be for - got - ten

1. above all the women on earth;
(1.) the creator of heaven and earth. **R/.**
2. by those who tell of the might of God. **R/.**

James M. Burns

B120 Thanksgiving Day
Revised
Psalm 145:2–3, 4–5, 6–7, 8–9, 10–11

RESPONSE: *cf. Psalm 145:1*

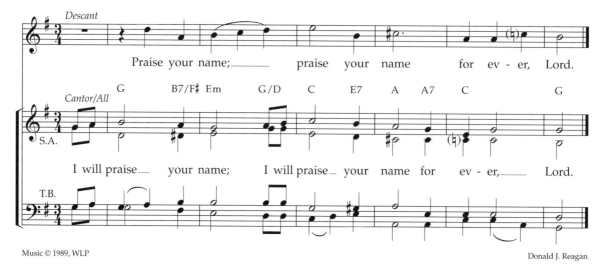

Praise your name;_____ praise your name for ev - er, Lord.

I will praise__ your name; I will praise__ your name for ev - er,_____ Lord.

Music © 1989, WLP

Donald J. Reagan

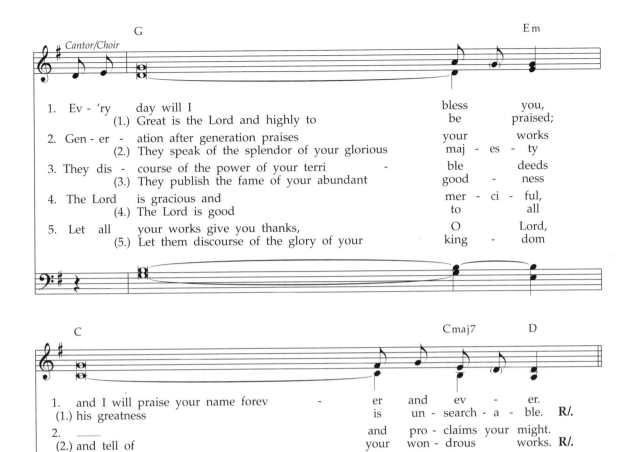

1. Ev - 'ry day will I bless you,
(1.) Great is the Lord and highly to be praised;
2. Gen - er - ation after generation praises your works
(2.) They speak of the splendor of your glorious maj - es - ty
3. They dis - course of the power of your terri - ble deeds
(3.) They publish the fame of your abundant good - ness
4. The Lord is gracious and mer - ci - ful,
(4.) The Lord is good to all
5. Let all your works give you thanks, O Lord,
(5.) Let them discourse of the glory of your king - dom

1. and I will praise your name forev - er and ev - er.
(1.) his greatness is un - search - a - ble. **R/.**
2. ____ and pro - claims your might.
(2.) and tell of your won - drous works. **R/.**
3. and de - clare your great - ness.
(3.) and joyfully sing of your jus - tice. **R/.**
4. slow to anger and of great kind - ness.
(4.) and compassionate toward all his works. **R/.**
5. and let your faith - ful ones bless you.
(5.) and speak of your might. **R/.**

Music © 2000, WLP

Tone 8G

[B121 is not needed in this revised edition]

World Day of Prayer for Peace
Psalm 72:2, 3–4ab, 7–8, 11–12, 13–14

RESPONSE: *cf. Psalm 72:7*

Music © 1971, WLP

Angelo A. della Picca

VERSES

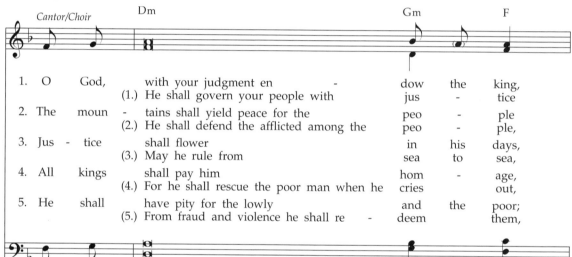

1. O God, with your judgment en - dow the king,
(1.) He shall govern your people with jus - tice

2. The moun - tains shall yield peace for the peo - ple
(2.) He shall defend the afflicted among the peo - ple,

3. Jus - tice shall flower in his days,
(3.) May he rule from sea to sea,

4. All kings shall pay him hom - age,
(4.) For he shall rescue the poor man when he cries out,

5. He shall have pity for the lowly and the poor;
(5.) From fraud and violence he shall re - deem them,

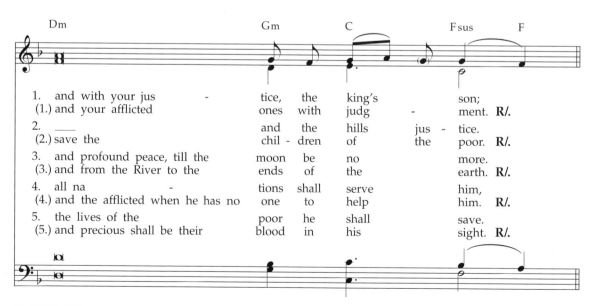

1. and with your jus - tice, the king's son;
(1.) and your afflicted ones with judg - ment. **R/.**

2. ____ and the hills jus - tice.
(2.) save the chil - dren of the poor. **R/.**

3. and profound peace, till the moon be no more.
(3.) and from the River to the ends of the earth. **R/.**

4. all na - tions shall serve him,
(4.) and the afflicted when he has no one to help him. **R/.**

5. the lives of the poor he shall save.
(5.) and precious shall be their blood in his sight. **R/.**

Music © 1981, WLP

Tone 1f, adapt.

RESPONSE: *Psalm 85:9*

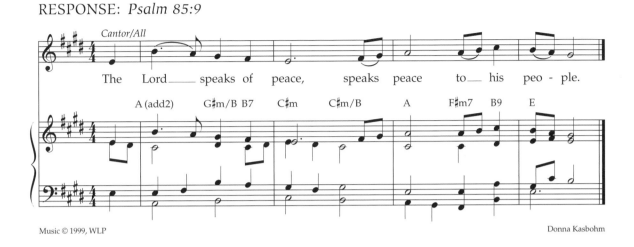

The Lord speaks of peace, speaks peace to his peo-ple.

Music © 1999, WLP

Donna Kasbohm

VERSES

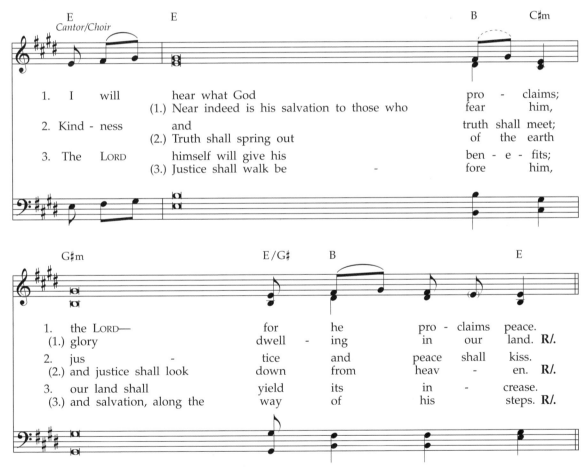

1. I will hear what God pro-claims;
(1.) Near indeed is his salvation to those who fear him,
2. Kind-ness and truth shall meet;
(2.) Truth shall spring out of the earth
3. The LORD himself will give his ben-e-fits;
(3.) Justice shall walk be-fore him,

1. the LORD— for he pro-claims peace.
(1.) glory dwell-ing in our land. **R/.**
2. jus-tice and peace shall kiss.
(2.) and justice shall look down from heav-en. **R/.**
3. our land shall yield its in-crease.
(3.) and salvation, along the way of his steps. **R/.**

Music © 1972, WLP

Tone 6

B124 Mass for the Dead
Revised
Psalm 23:1–3, 4, 5, 6

RESPONSE: *Psalm 23:1*

The Lord___ is my shep - herd;__ there is noth - ing I___ shall want.

Music © 1970, WLP

Angelo A. della Picca

VERSES

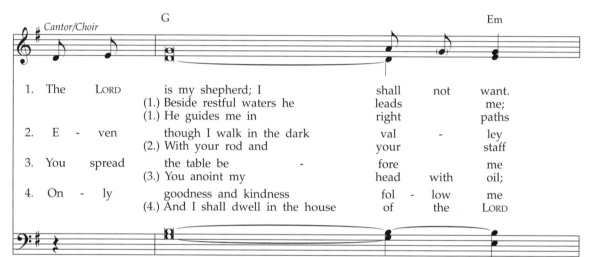

Cantor/Choir

1. The LORD	is my shepherd; I	shall	not	want.
(1.) Beside restful waters he	leads	me;
(1.) He guides me in	right	paths
2. E - ven	though I walk in the dark	val -	ley
(2.) With your rod and	your	staff
3. You spread	the table be -	fore	me
(3.) You anoint my	head with	oil;
4. On - ly	goodness and kindness	fol - low	me
(4.) And I shall dwell in the house	of the	LORD

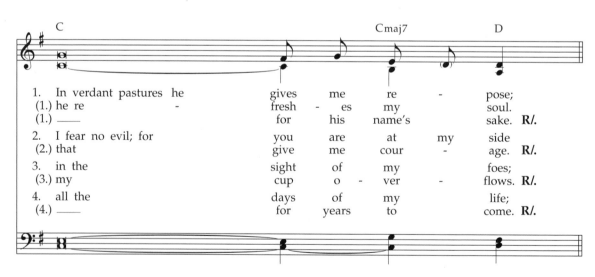

1. In verdant pastures he	gives	me	re -	pose;
(1.) he re -	fresh -	es	my	soul. **R/.**
(1.) ___	for	his	name's	sake. **R/.**
2. I fear no evil; for	you	are	at	my side
(2.) that	give	me	cour -	age. **R/.**
3. in the	sight	of	my	foes;
(3.) my	cup	o -	ver -	flows. **R/.**
4. all the	days	of	my	life;
(4.) ___	for	years	to	come. **R/.**

Music © 2000, WLP

Tone 8G

Mass for the Dead B125
Psalm 27:1, 4, 7, 8b, 9a, 13–14

RESPONSE: *Psalm 27:1a*

Music © 1970, WLP

James M. Burns

VERSES

1. The LORD is my light and my sal - va - tion;
(1.) The LORD is my life's ref - uge;

2. One thing I ask of the LORD;
(2.) To dwell in the house of the LORD
(2.) That I may gaze on the loveliness of the LORD

3. Hear, O LORD, the sound of my call;
(3.) Your presence, O LORD, I seek.

4. I be - lieve that I shall see the bounty of the LORD
(4.) Wait for the LORD with cour - age;

1. whom should I fear?
(1.) of whom should I be a - fraid? **R/.**

2. ___ this I seek:
(2.) all the days of my life,
(2.) and contemplate his tem - ple. **R/.**

3. have pity on me, and an - swer me.
(3.) Hide not your face from me. **R/.**

4. in the land of the liv - ing.
(4.) be stouthearted, and wait for the LORD. **R/.**

Music © 1981, WLP

James M. Burns

B126 Mass for the Dead
Psalm 103:8, 10, 13–14, 15–16, 17–18

RESPONSE: *Psalm 103:8a*

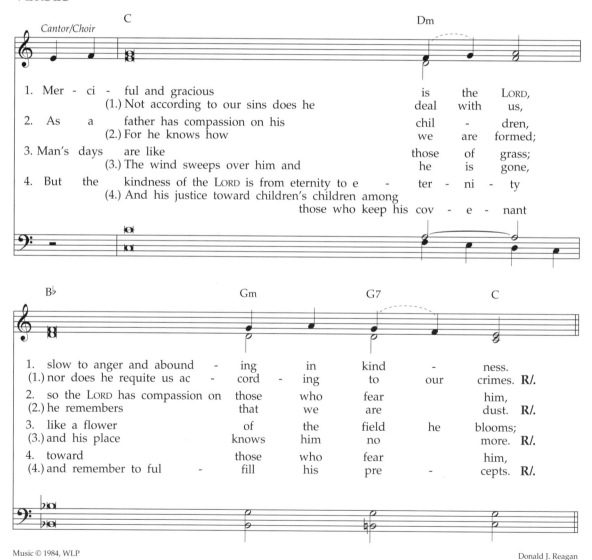

The Lord___ is kind___ and mer - ci - ful. mer - ci - ful.

Music © 1982, WLP

Donald J. Reagan

VERSES

1. Mer - ci - ful and gracious   is the Lord,
(1.) Not according to our sins does he   deal with us,
2. As a father has compassion on his   chil - dren,
(2.) For he knows how   we are formed;
3. Man's days are like   those of grass;
(3.) The wind sweeps over him and   he is gone,
4. But the kindness of the Lord is from eternity to e - ter - ni - ty
(4.) And his justice toward children's children among those who keep his cov - e - nant

1. slow to anger and abound - ing in kind - ness.
(1.) nor does he requite us ac - cord - ing to our crimes. **R/.**
2. so the Lord has compassion on those who fear him,
(2.) he remembers that we are dust. **R/.**
3. like a flower of the field he blooms;
(3.) and his place knows him no more. **R/.**
4. toward those who fear him,
(4.) and remember to ful - fill his pre - cepts. **R/.**

Music © 1984, WLP

Donald J. Reagan

Revised

Mass for the Dead
Psalm 116:5, 6, 10–11, 15–16ac

RESPONSE: *Psalm 116:9*

Cantor/All

I will walk in the pres-ence of the Lord, in the land of the liv - ing.

Howard Hughes

A sung Alleluia *may replace this response.*

VERSES

1. Gra - cious is the LORD and just;
2. The LORD keeps the lit - tle ones;
3. I be - lieved, even when I said,
(3.) I said in my a - larm
4. Pre - cious in the eyes of the LORD
(4.) O LORD, I am your serv - ant,

1. yes, our God is mer - ci - ful. **R/.**
2. I was brought low, and he saved me. **R/.**
3. "I am great - ly af - flict - ed";
(3.) "No man is de - pend - a - ble." **R/.**
4. is the death of his faith - ful ones.
(4.) you have loosed my bonds. **R/.**

Tone 6

B128 Mass for the Dead
Revised
Psalm 130:1–2, 3–4, 5–6a, 6b–7, 8

RESPONSE: *Psalm 130:7*

Out of the depths I cry to you, O Lord.

Music © 1993, WLP

Mike Hay, 1953–1999

VERSES

Cantor/Choir

1. Out of the depths I cry to you, O LORD;
(1.) Let your ears be at - ten - tive
2. If you, O LORD, mark in - iq - ui - ties,
(2.) But with you is for - give - ness,
3. I trust in the LORD;
(3.) My soul waits for the LORD
4. More than sentinels wait for the dawn,
(4.) For with the LORD is kind - ness
5. And he will redeem Is - ra - el

1. ___ LORD, hear my voice! R/.
(1.) to my voice in sup - pli - ca - tion. R/.
2. ___ LORD, who can stand? R/.
(2.) that you may be re - vered. R/.
3. my soul trusts in his word. R/.
(3.) more than sentinels wait for the dawn. R/.
4. let Israel wait for the LORD, R/.
(4.) and with him is plen - teous re - demp - tions. R/.
5. from all their in - iq - ui - ties. R/.

Music © 1984, WLP

Howard L. Hughes

B129 Common Psalm—Season of Advent
Psalm 25:1, 4–5, 8–9, 10, 14

RESPONSE: *Psalm 25:1*

To you, O___ Lord, I lift my soul.

Music © 1990, WLP

James J. Chepponis

Music © 1990, WLP

James J. Chepponis

VERSES

1. Your ways, O LORD, make   known   to   me;
(1.) Guide me in your truth and   teach   me,

2. Good and upright   is   the   LORD;
(2.) He guides the humble to   jus - tice

3. All the paths of the LORD are kindness and   con - stan - cy
(3.) The friendship of the LORD is with those who   fear   him,

1. teach   me   your   paths.
(1.) for you are God my   sav - ior. **R/.**

2. thus he shows sinners   the   way.
(2.) and teaches the humble   his   way. **R/.**

3. toward those who keep his covenant and   his   de - crees.
(3.) and his covenant for their in - struc - tion. **R/.**

Music © 1997, WLP

Steven R. Janco

VERSE 1

1. Your ways, O LORD, make known to me; teach me your paths.

1. Guide me in your truth and teach me, for you are God my sav - ior.

VERSE 2

2. Good and up-right is the LORD; thus he shows sin - ners the way. He

2. guides the hum - ble to jus - tice and teach-es the hum - ble his way.

VERSE 3

3. All the LORD'S paths are kind-ness and con-stan-cy toward those who keep his de -

3. crees. The LORD'S friend-ship is with those who fear him, and his

3. cov - e-nant for their in - struc - tion.

James J. Chepponis

B130 Common Psalm—Season of Advent
Psalm 85:9–10, 11–12, 13–14

RESPONSE: *Psalm 85:8a*

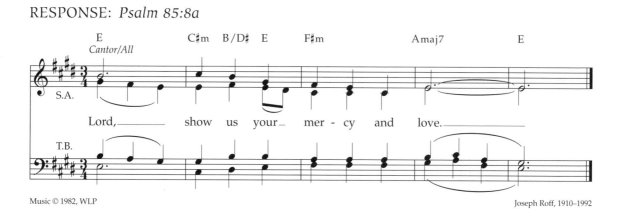

Lord, show us your mer-cy and love.

Music © 1982, WLP

Joseph Roff, 1910–1992

VERSES

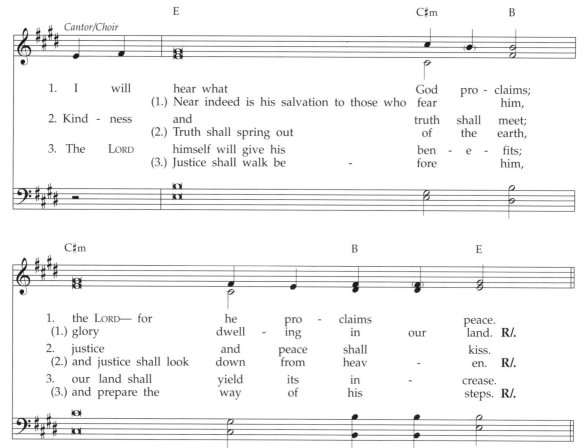

1. I will hear what God pro - claims;
(1.) Near indeed is his salvation to those who fear him,
2. Kind - ness and truth shall meet;
(2.) Truth shall spring out of the earth,
3. The LORD himself will give his ben - e - fits;
(3.) Justice shall walk be - fore him,

1. the LORD— for he pro - claims our peace.
(1.) glory dwell - ing in our land. **R/.**
2. justice and peace shall kiss.
(2.) and justice shall look down from heav - en. **R/.**
3. our land shall yield its in - crease.
(3.) and prepare the way of his steps. **R/.**

Music © 1982, WLP

Joseph Roff, 1910–1992

Common Psalm—Season of Christmas B131
Psalm 98:1, 2–3ab, 3cd–4, 5–6

RESPONSE: *Psalm 98:3cd*

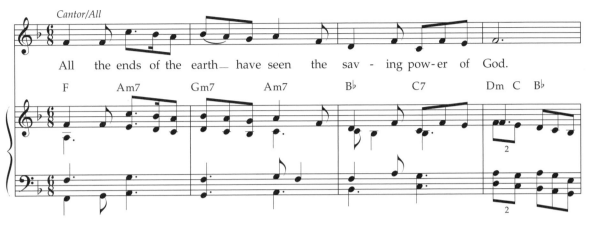

Music © 1995, WLP

Steven R. Janco

VERSES

1. Sing to the LORD a new song, _____ for he has done won-drous

2. The LORD has made his sal - va - tion known, re - veal-ing his jus - tice to the

3. All the ends of the earth have seen the sal - va - tion by our

4. Sing praise to the LORD with the harp, _____ with harp and mel - o - dious

B♭m7   Cm7   F(add2)   B♭m7   G♭

1. deeds; _____ His right hand has won the vic - t'ry for him, _____

2. na - tions. _____ He has re - mem - bered his kind - ness and faith - ful - ness ____

3. God. _____ Sing joy - ful - ly ____ to the LORD, all you lands; _____

4. song. _____ With trum - pets ____ and the sound of the horn _____

F   F7   B♭m7   Cm7   D♭maj7   E♭

To Response

1. __ his ho - ly arm. _____

To Response

2. __ toward Is - ra - el. _____

To Response

3. __ sing praise to God. _____

To Response

4. __ sing to our King. _____

Gm7   Gm9   Csus   C   Gm7   C

To Response

Steven R. Janco

or

F   Am7

Cantor/Choir

1. Sing to the LORD   a   new   song,
(1.) his right hand has won vic   -   t'ry   for   him,

2. The LORD has made his sal   -   va   -   tion   known:
(2.) He has remembered his kindness and his   faith   -   ful   -   ness

3. All the ends of the   earth   have   seen
(3.) Sing joyfully to the LORD,   all   you   lands;

4. Sing praise to the LORD   with   the   harp,
(4.) With trumpets and the sound   of   the   horn

B♭   Gm   C

1. for he has done   won - drous   deeds;
(1.) his   ho - ly   arm. **R/.**

2. in the sight of the nations he has revealed his   jus - tice.
(2.) toward the house of   Is - ra - el. **R/.**

3. the salvation   by   our   God.
(3.) break into song;   sing   praise. **R/.**

4. with the harp and me   -   lo - dious   song.
(4.) sing joyfully before the   King,   the   LORD. **R/.**

Steven R. Janco

B132 Common Psalm—Season of Lent
Psalm 51:3–4, 5–6, 12–13, 14, 17

RESPONSE: *cf. Psalm 51:3a*

Be mer-ci-ful, be mer-ci-ful, be mer-ci-ful, O Lord.

Be mer-ci-ful, O Lord, for we have sinned.

Michael Ward

VERSES

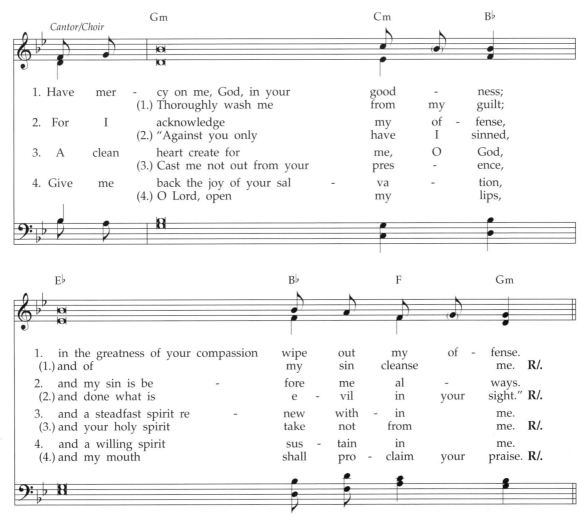

1. Have mer - cy on me, God, in your good - ness;
(1.) Thoroughly wash me from my guilt;
2. For I acknowledge my of - fense,
(2.) "Against you only have I sinned,
3. A clean heart create for me, O God,
(3.) Cast me not out from your pres - ence,
4. Give me back the joy of your sal - va - tion,
(4.) O Lord, open my lips,

1. in the greatness of your compassion wipe out my of - fense.
(1.) and of my sin cleanse me. **R/.**
2. and my sin is be - fore me al - ways.
(2.) and done what is e - vil in your sight." **R/.**
3. and a steadfast spirit re - new with - in me.
(3.) and your holy spirit take not from me. **R/.**
4. and a willing spirit sus - tain in me.
(4.) and my mouth shall pro - claim your praise. **R/.**

Tone 2

B133 Common Psalm—Season of Lent
Psalm 91:1–2, 10–11, 12–13, 14, 16

RESPONSE: *cf. Psalm 91:15b*

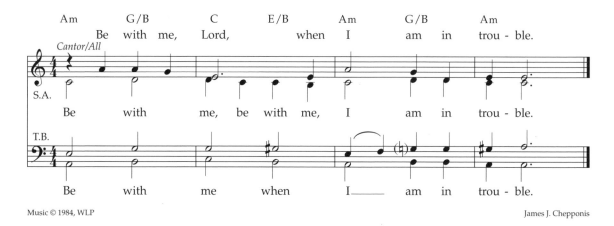

Music © 1984, WLP

James J. Chepponis

VERSES

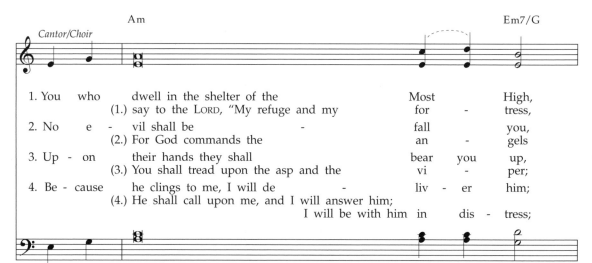

1. You who dwell in the shelter of the Most High,
(1.) say to the LORD, "My refuge and my for - tress,
2. No e - vil shall be - fall you,
(2.) For God commands the an - gels
3. Up - on their hands they shall bear you up,
(3.) You shall tread upon the asp and the vi - per;
4. Be - cause he clings to me, I will de - liv - er him;
(4.) He shall call upon me, and I will answer him;
I will be with him in dis - tress;

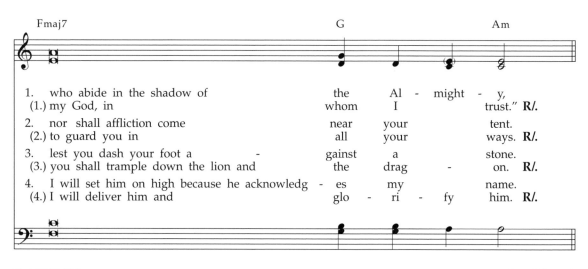

1. who abide in the shadow of the Al - might - y,
(1.) my God, in whom I trust." **R/.**
2. nor shall affliction come near your tent.
(2.) to guard you in all your ways. **R/.**
3. lest you dash your foot a - gainst a stone.
(3.) you shall trample down the lion and the drag - on. **R/.**
4. I will set him on high because he acknowledg - es my name.
(4.) I will deliver him and glo - ri - fy him. **R/.**

Music © 1984, WLP

James J. Chepponis

Common Psalm—Season of Lent B134
Psalm 130:1–2, 3–4, 4–6, 7–8

RESPONSE: *Psalm 130:7bc*

With the Lord there is mer-cy and full-ness of re-demp-tion.

Music © 1999, WLP

Michael Bogdan

VERSES

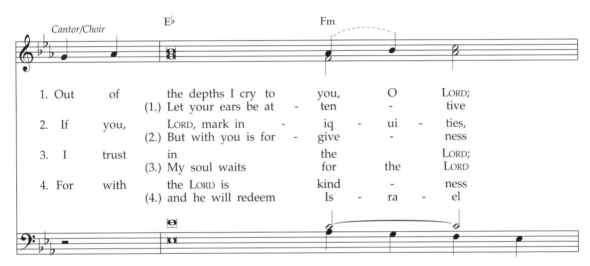

Cantor/Choir

1. Out of the depths I cry to you, O Lord;
(1.) Let your ears be at - ten - tive
2. If you, Lord, mark in - iq - ui - ties,
(2.) But with you is for - give - ness
3. I trust in the Lord;
(3.) My soul waits for the Lord
4. For with the Lord is kind - ness
(4.) and he will redeem Is - ra - el

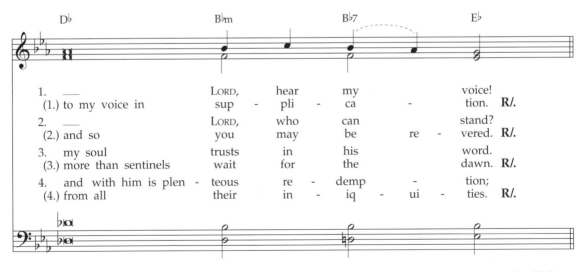

1. — Lord, hear my voice!
(1.) to my voice in sup - pli - ca - tion. **R/.**
2. — Lord, who can stand?
(2.) and so you may be re - vered. **R/.**
3. my soul trusts in his word.
(3.) more than sentinels wait for the dawn. **R/.**
4. and with him is plen - teous re - demp - tion;
(4.) from all their in - iq - ui - ties. **R/.**

Music © 1984, WLP

Donald J. Reagan

B135 Common Psalm—Holy Week
Psalm 22:8–9, 17–18, 19–20, 23–24

RESPONSE: *Psalm 22:2a*

Am9   Cmaj7/G   Am   Am9   Am   B♭maj7   Gm   Am

Cantor/All

My God,   my God,   why have you a‑ban‑doned me?

Music © 1984, WLP   Jerry R. Brubaker

VERSES

Am   Am7/G

Cantor/Choir

1.   All who see me   scoff   at   me;
(1.) "He relied on the LORD; let him de - liv - er him,

2.   Many dogs   sur - round me,
(2.) They have pierced my hands   and   my   feet;

3.   They divide my garments a - mong them,
(3.) But you, O LORD, be not   far   from   me;

4.   I will proclaim your name to my   breth - ren;
(4.) "You who fear the Lord,   praise   him;

Fmaj7   Dm7   E(no 3rd)

1.   they mock me with parted lips, they   wag   their   heads:
(1.) let him rescue him, if   he   loves   him." **R/.**

2.   a pack of evildoers closes in up - on   me;
(2.) I can count   all   my   bones. **R/.**

3.   and for my vesture   they   cast   lots.
(3.) O my help, hasten to   aid   me. **R/.**

4.   in the midst of the assembly I will   praise   you:
(4.) all you descendants of Jacob, give glory to him;
       revere him, all you descendants of Is - ra - el!" **R/.**

Music © 1997, WLP   Steven R. Janco

B136 Common Psalm—Easter Vigil
Psalm 136:1–3, 4–6, 7–9, 24–26;
Psalm 136:1, 3, 16, 21–23, 24–26

RESPONSE:

God's love is ev-er-last - ing; God's love is ev-er-last - ing.

G   Cmaj7   B7   Em   Am7   Am7/D   Fmaj7   G

God's love is ev-er-last - ing; God's love is ev-er-last - ing.

Music © 1987, WLP

Paul A. Lisicky

VERSES

G/B   D   Em

1. Give thanks to the LORD, for   he is good,
(1.) give thanks to the   God of gods,
(1.) give thanks to the   LORD of lords,

2. Who a - lone does great   won - ders,
(2.) who made the heavens in   wis - dom,
(2.) who spread out the earth upon the   wa - ters,

3. Who made the   great lights,
(3.) the sun to rule over   the day,
(3.) the moon and the stars to rule over the   night,

4. Who freed us   from our foes,
(4.) who gives food to   all flesh,
(4.) give thanks to the God of   heav - en,

C   D7/C   Cmaj7   D

1.–4. for his mercy en - dures for - ev - er;
(1.–4.) for his mercy en - dures for - ev - er;
(1.–4.) for his mercy en - dures for - ev - er. **R/.**

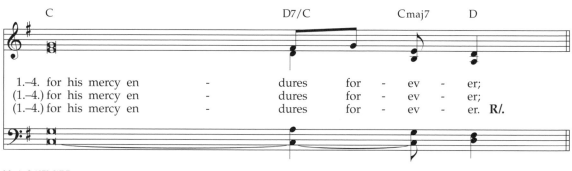

Music © 1972, WLP

Tone 8G

VERSES

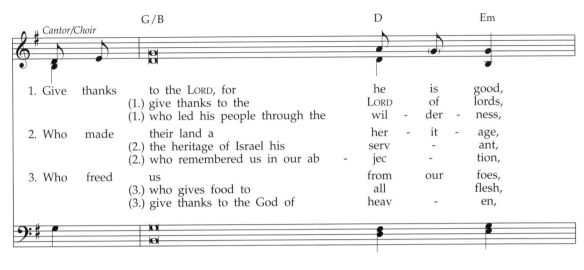

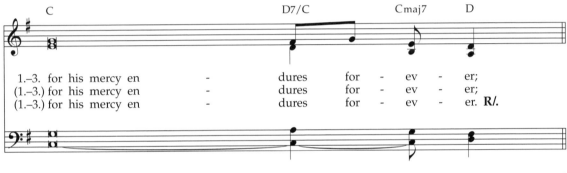

1. Give thanks to the LORD, for he is good,
(1.) give thanks to the LORD of lords,
(1.) who led his people through the wil - der - ness,

2. Who made their land a her - it - age,
(2.) the heritage of Israel his serv - ant,
(2.) who remembered us in our ab - jec - tion,

3. Who freed us from our foes,
(3.) who gives food to all flesh,
(3.) give thanks to the God of heav - en,

1.–3. for his mercy en - dures for - ev - er;
(1.–3.) for his mercy en - dures for - ev - er;
(1.–3.) for his mercy en - dures for - ev - er. **R/.**

Tone 8G

B137 Common Psalm—Season of Easter
Psalm 118:1–2, 16–17, 22–24

RESPONSE: *Psalm 118:24*

Alan J. Hommerding

VERSES*

Music © 1994, WLP

Alan J. Hommerding

Verses with psalm tone on next page.

VERSES

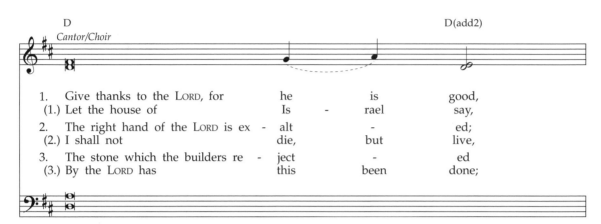

1. Give thanks to the LORD, for he is good,
(1.) Let the house of Is - rael say,
2. The right hand of the LORD is ex - alt - ed;
(2.) I shall not die, but live,
3. The stone which the builders re - ject - ed
(3.) By the LORD has this been done;

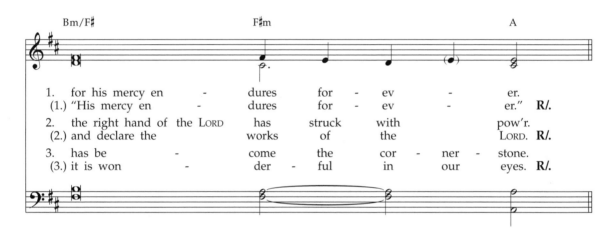

1. for his mercy en - dures for - ev - er.
(1.) "His mercy en - dures for - ev - er." **R/.**
2. the right hand of the LORD has struck with pow'r.
(2.) and declare the works of the LORD. **R/.**
3. has be - come the cor - ner - stone.
(3.) it is won - der - ful in our eyes. **R/.**

Alan J. Hommerding

Common Psalm—Season of Easter   B138
Psalm 66:1–3, 4–5, 6–7, 16, 20

RESPONSE: *Psalm 66:1*

Let all the earth___ cry out to God with joy, al - le - lu - ia.

John H. Olivier

VERSES

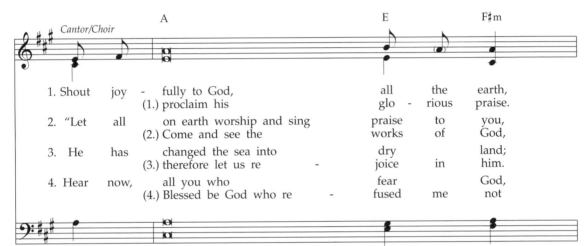

1. Shout joy - fully to God,   all   the   earth,
   (1.) proclaim his   glo -   rious   praise.
2. "Let all   on earth worship and sing   praise   to   you,
   (2.) Come and see the   works   of   God,
3. He has   changed the sea into   dry   land;
   (3.) therefore let us re -   joice   in   him.
4. Hear now,   all you who   fear   God,
   (4.) Blessed be God who re -   fused   me   not

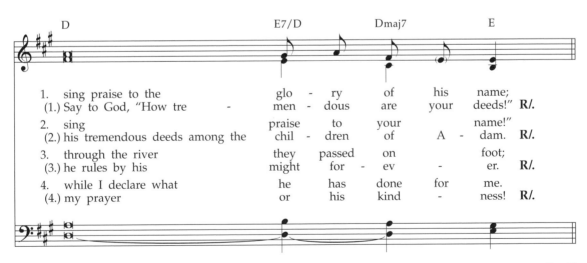

1. sing praise to the   glo - ry   of   his   name;
   (1.) Say to God, "How tre - men - dous   are   your   deeds!" **R/.**
2. sing   praise   to   your   name!"
   (2.) his tremendous deeds among the   chil - dren   of   A - dam. **R/.**
3. through the river   they   passed   on   foot;
   (3.) he rules by his   might   for - ev - er. **R/.**
4. while I declare what   he   has   done   for   me.
   (4.) my prayer   or   his   kind - ness! **R/.**

Tone 8G

B139 Common Psalm—Pentecost
Psalm 104:1, 24, 29–31, 34

RESPONSE: *cf. Psalm 104:30*

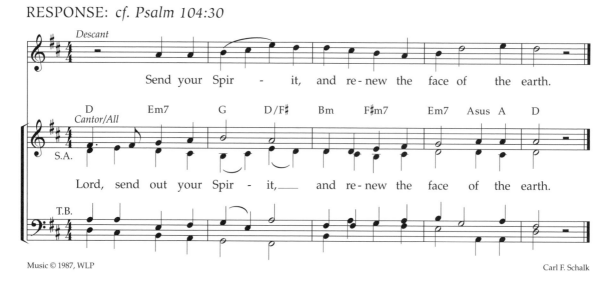

Send your Spir - it, and re-new the face of the earth.

Lord, send out your Spir - it,___ and re-new the face of the earth.

Music © 1987, WLP

Carl F. Schalk

VERSES

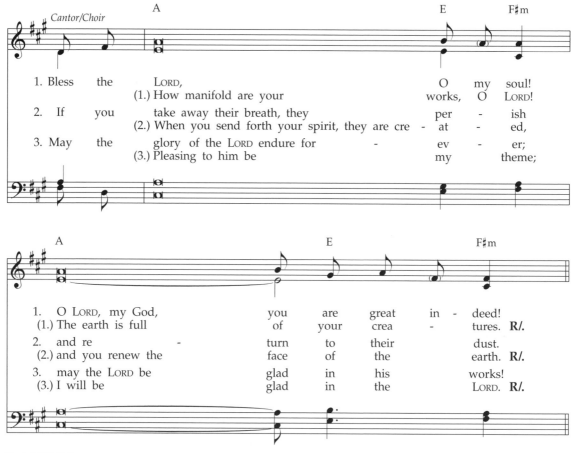

1. Bless the LORD, O my soul!
(1.) How manifold are your works, O LORD!
2. If you take away their breath, they per - ish
(2.) When you send forth your spirit, they are cre - at - ed,
3. May the glory of the LORD endure for - ev - er;
(3.) Pleasing to him be my theme;

1. O LORD, my God, you are great in - deed!
(1.) The earth is full of your crea - tures. **R/.**
2. and re - turn to their dust.
(2.) and you renew the face of the earth. **R/.**
3. may the LORD be glad in his works!
(3.) I will be glad in the LORD. **R/.**

Music © 1972, WLP

Tone 5

Common Psalm—Ordinary Time   B140
Psalm 19:8, 9, 10. 11

RESPONSE: *John 6:68c*

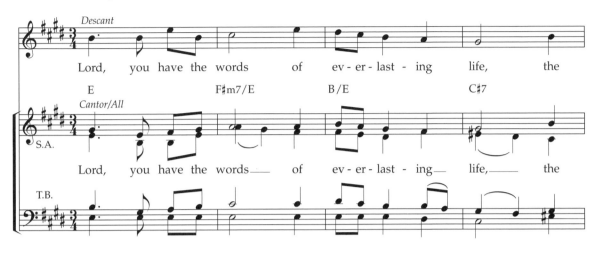

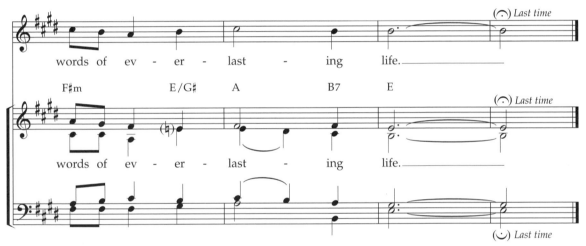

Music © 1987, WLP

Marty Haugen

Marty Haugen

Cantor/Choir
D · A/C♯ · Am/C

1. The law of the Lord is per - fect, re - fresh - ing the
2. The pre - cepts of the Lord are right,_____ re - joic - ing the
3. The fear of the Lord is pure,_____ en - dur - ing for
4. They are more pre - cious than____ gold, than a heap of pur - est

E/B · Amaj7 · G♯m7 · C♯m

1. soul. The de - cree of the Lord is trust - wor - thy, giv - ing
2. heart. The com - mand of the Lord is clear,_____ en -
3. ev - er.____ The____ ord - 'nan - ces of the Lord are true,
4. gold; sweet - er al - so than syr - up____ or

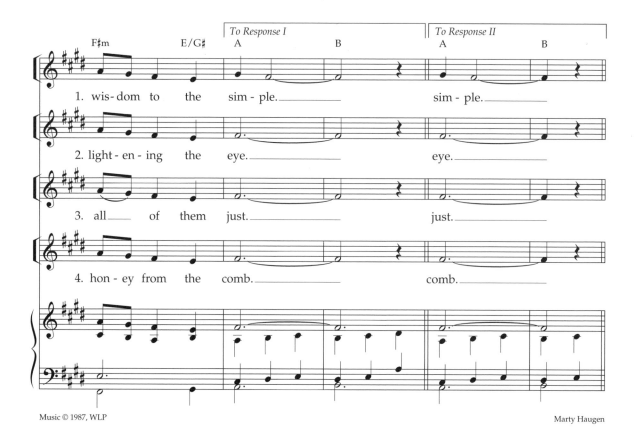

Marty Haugen

VERSES

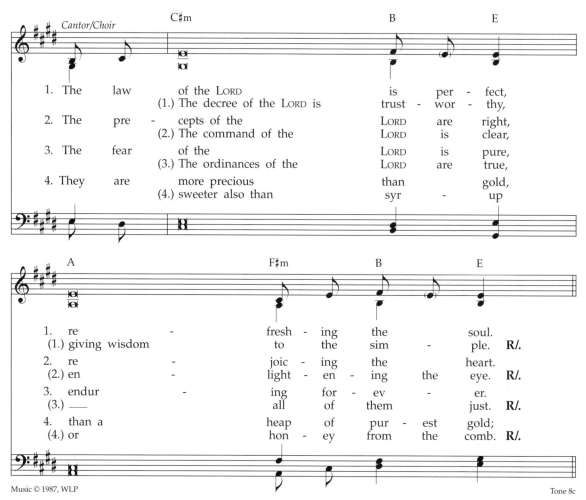

Cantor/Choir

1. The law of the LORD is per - fect,
   (1.) The decree of the LORD is trust - wor - thy,
2. The pre - cepts of the LORD are right,
   (2.) The command of the LORD is clear,
3. The fear of the LORD is pure,
   (3.) The ordinances of the LORD are true,
4. They are more precious than gold,
   (4.) sweeter also than syr - up

1. re - fresh - ing the soul.
   (1.) giving wisdom to the sim - ple. **R/.**
2. re - joic - ing the heart.
   (2.) en - light - en - ing the eye. **R/.**
3. endur - ing for - ev - er.
   (3.) —— all of them just. **R/.**
4. than a heap of pur - est gold;
   (4.) or hon - ey from the comb. **R/.**

Tone 8c

Common Psalm—Ordinary Time B141
Psalm 27:1, 4, 13–14

RESPONSE: *Psalm 27:1a*

Music © 1970, WLP

James M. Burns

VERSES

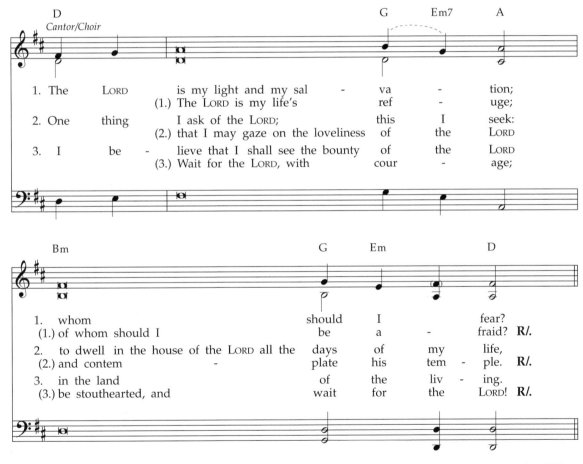

1. The Lord is my light and my sal - va - tion;
(1.) The Lord is my life's ref - uge;
2. One thing I ask of the Lord; this I seek:
(2.) that I may gaze on the loveliness of the Lord
3. I be - lieve that I shall see the bounty of the Lord
(3.) Wait for the Lord, with cour - age;

1. whom should I fear?
(1.) of whom should I be a - fraid? **R/.**
2. to dwell in the house of the Lord all the days of my life,
(2.) and contem - plate his tem - ple. **R/.**
3. in the land of the liv - ing.
(3.) be stouthearted, and wait for the Lord! **R/.**

Music © 1984, WLP

James M. Burns

B142 Common Psalm—Ordinary Time
Psalm 34:2–3, 4–5, 6–7. 8–9

RESPONSE: *Psalm 34:2*

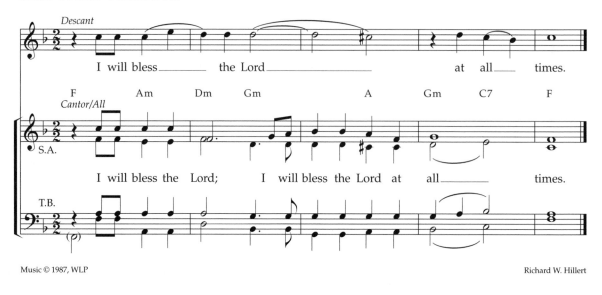

I will bless the Lord at all times.

I will bless the Lord; I will bless the Lord at all times.

Richard W. Hillert

or

RESPONSE: *Psalm 34:9a*

Taste and see the good-ness of the Lord.

Taste and see; taste and see the good-ness of the Lord.

Richard W. Hillert

VERSES

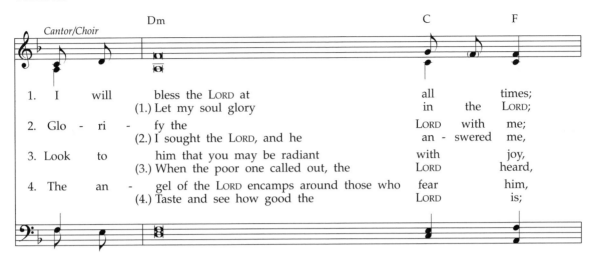

1. I will bless the Lord at all times;
   (1.) Let my soul glory in the Lord;
2. Glo - ri - fy the Lord with me;
   (2.) I sought the Lord, and he an - swered me,
3. Look to him that you may be radiant with joy,
   (3.) When the poor one called out, the Lord heard,
4. The an - gel of the Lord encamps around those who fear him,
   (4.) Taste and see how good the Lord is;

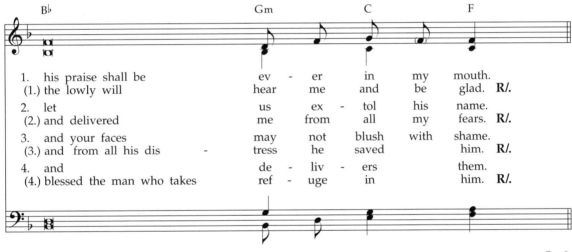

1. his praise shall be ev - er in my mouth.
   (1.) the lowly will hear me and be glad. **R/.**
2. let us ex - tol his name.
   (2.) and delivered me from all my fears. **R/.**
3. and your faces may not blush with shame.
   (3.) and from all his dis - tress he saved him. **R/.**
4. and de - liv - ers them.
   (4.) blessed the man who takes ref - uge in him. **R/.**

Tone 8c

B143 Common Psalm—Ordinary Time
Psalm 63:2, 3–4, 5–6, 8–9

RESPONSE: *Psalm 63:2b*

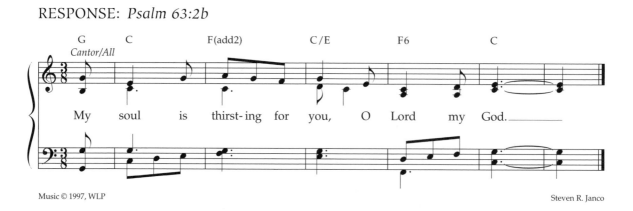

My soul is thirst-ing for you, O Lord my God.

Steven R. Janco

VERSES

Cantor/Choir

1. O God, you are my God, whom I seek; for you my flesh pines and my soul thirsts
2. Thus have I gazed toward you in the sanctu - ar - y
(2.)For your kindness is a greater good than life;
3. Thus will I bless you as I live;
(3.)As with the riches of a banquet shall my soul be sat - is - fied,
4. You are my help,
(4.)My soul clings fast to you;

1. like the earth, parched, lifeless and without wa - ter. **R/.**
2. to see your power and your glo - ry,
(2.) my lips shall glo - ri - fy you. **R/.**
3. lifting up my hands, I will call up - on your name.
(3.) and with exultant lips my mouth shall praise you. **R/.**
4. and in the shadow of your wings I shout for joy.
(4.) your right hand up - holds me. **R/.**

Steven R. Janco

Common Psalm—Ordinary Time B144
Psalm 95:1–2, 6–7, 8–9

RESPONSE: *Psalm 95:8*

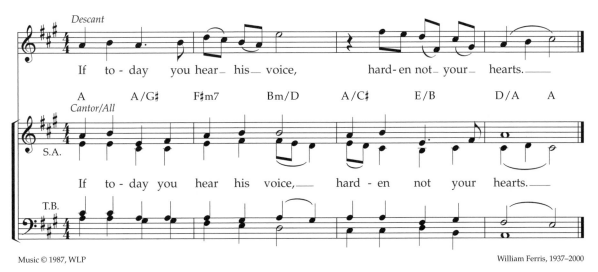

If to-day you hear his voice, hard-en not your hearts.

If to-day you hear his voice, hard-en not your hearts.

Music © 1987, WLP

William Ferris, 1937–2000

VERSES

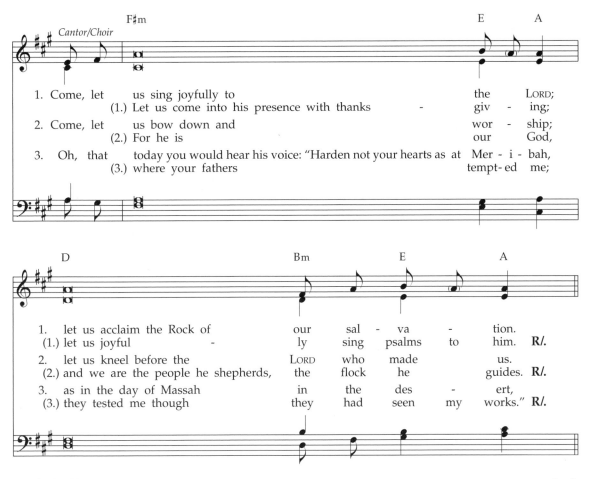

1. Come, let us sing joyfully to the LORD;
(1.) Let us come into his presence with thanks - giv - ing;
2. Come, let us bow down and wor - ship;
(2.) For he is our God,
3. Oh, that today you would hear his voice: "Harden not your hearts as at Mer - i - bah,
(3.) where your fathers tempt-ed me;

1. let us acclaim the Rock of our sal - va - tion.
(1.) let us joyful - ly sing psalms to him. **R/.**
2. let us kneel before the LORD who made us.
(2.) and we are the people he shepherds, the flock he guides. **R/.**
3. as in the day of Massah in the des - ert,
(3.) they tested me though they had seen my works." **R/.**

Music © 1972, WLP

Tone 8c

B145 Common Psalm—Ordinary Time
Psalm 100:2, 3, 5

RESPONSE: *Psalm 100:3c*

We are his peo-ple: the sheep of his flock.

Music © 1999, WLP

Michael Bogdan

VERSES

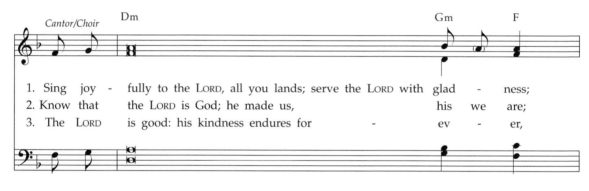

1. Sing joy-fully to the LORD, all you lands; serve the LORD with glad - ness;
2. Know that the LORD is God; he made us, his we are;
3. The LORD is good: his kindness endures for - ev - er,

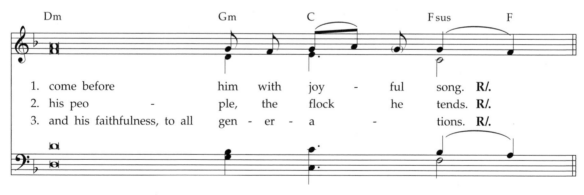

1. come before him with joy - ful song. **R/.**
2. his peo - ple, the flock he tends. **R/.**
3. and his faithfulness, to all gen - er - a - tions. **R/.**

Music © 1972, WLP

Tone 1f, adapt.

Common Psalm—Ordinary Time B146
Psalm 103:1–2, 3–4, 8, 10, 12–13

RESPONSE: *Psalm 103:8*

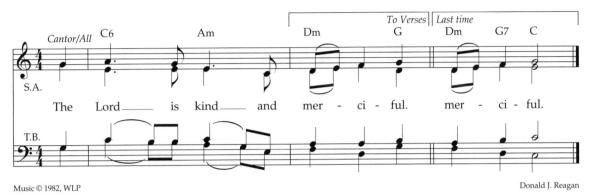

Music © 1982, WLP   Donald J. Reagan

VERSES

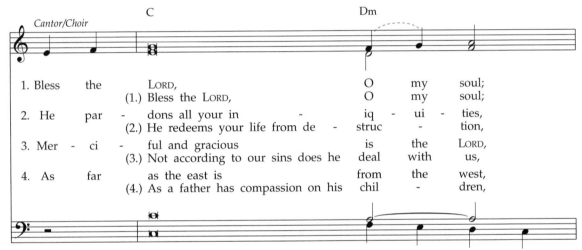

1. Bless the LORD, O my soul;
(1.) Bless the LORD, O my soul;
2. He par - dons all your in - iq - ui - ties,
(2.) He redeems your life from de - struc - tion,
3. Mer - ci - ful and gracious is the LORD,
(3.) Not according to our sins does he deal with us,
4. As far as the east is from the west,
(4.) As a father has compassion on his chil - dren,

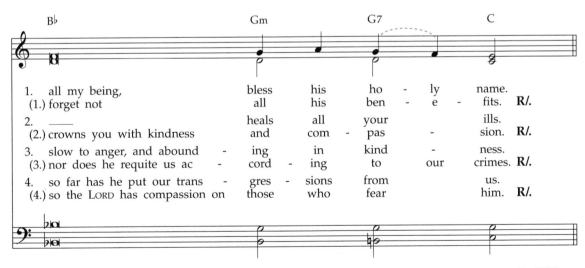

1. all my being, bless his ho - ly name.
(1.) forget not all his ben - e - fits. **R/.**
2. _____ heals all your ills.
(2.) crowns you with kindness and com - pas - sion. **R/.**
3. slow to anger, and abound - ing in kind - ness.
(3.) nor does he requite us ac - cord - ing to our crimes. **R/.**
4. so far has he put our trans - gres - sions from us.
(4.) so the LORD has compassion on those who fear him. **R/.**

Music © 1984, WLP   Donald J. Reagan

B147 Common Psalm—Ordinary Time
Psalm 145:1–2, 8–9, 10–11, 13–14

RESPONSE: *cf. Psalm 145:1*

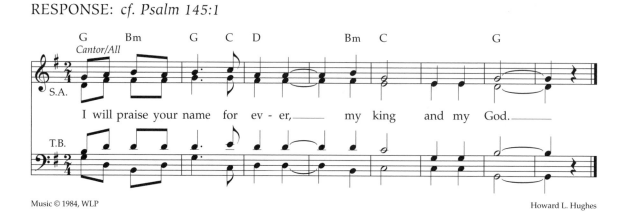

Music © 1984, WLP

Howard L. Hughes

VERSES

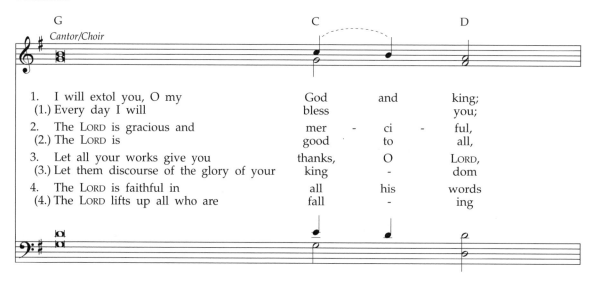

1. I will extol you, O my **God** **and** **king;**
(1.) Every day I will **bless** **you;**
2. The LORD is gracious and **mer** - **ci** - **ful,**
(2.) The LORD is **good** **to** **all,**
3. Let all your works give you **thanks,** **O** **LORD,**
(3.) Let them discourse of the glory of your **king** - **dom**
4. The LORD is faithful in **all** **his** **words**
(4.) The LORD lifts up all who are **fall** - **ing**

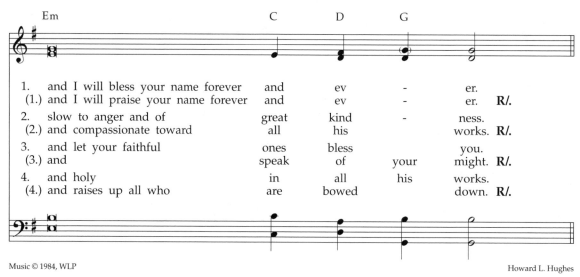

1. and I will bless your name forever **and** **ev** - **er.**
(1.) and I will praise your name forever **and** **ev** - **er.** **R/.**
2. slow to anger and of **great** **kind** - **ness.**
(2.) and compassionate toward **all** **his** **works.** **R/.**
3. and let your faithful **ones** **bless** **you.**
(3.) and **speak** **of** **your** **might.** **R/.**
4. and holy **in** **all** **his** **works.**
(4.) and raises up all who **are** **bowed** **down.** **R/.**

Music © 1984, WLP

Howard L. Hughes

RESPONSE: *cf. Psalm 122:1*

Let us go rejoicing to the house of the Lord.

Music © 1984, WLP   Eugene E. Englert

VERSES

1. I   re - joiced because they   said   to   me,
   (1.) And now we have   set   foot
2. Je - ru - salem, built as a   cit - y
   (2.) To it the   tribes   go   up,
3. Ac - cord - ing to the decree for   Is - ra - el,
   (3.) In it are set up   judg - ment   seats,
4. Pray   for   the peace of Je - ru - sa - lem!
   (4.) May peace be with - in   your   walls,
5. Be - cause   of my relatives   and   friends
   (5.) Because of the house of the   Lord,   our   God,

1. "We will go up to the   house   of   the   Lord."
   (1.) within your gates,   O   Je - ru - sa - lem. **R/.**
2. with   com - pact   u - ni - ty.
   (2.) the   tribes   of   the   Lord. **R/.**
3. to give thanks to the   name   of   the   Lord.
   (3.) seats for the   house   of   Da - vid. **R/.**
4. May those who   love   you   pros - per!
   (4.) prosperity   in   your   build - ings. **R/.**
5. I will say, "Peace   be   with - in   you!"
   (5.) I will   pray   for   your   good. **R/.**

Music © 1972, WLP   Tone 5

B149 Gospel Acclamation

Revised

RESPONSE

Al-le-lu - ia, al - le-lu - ia, al-le-lu - ia, al-le-lu - ia.

Music © 1998, WLP

Paul M. French

Choral harmony may be found at B172.

VERSES

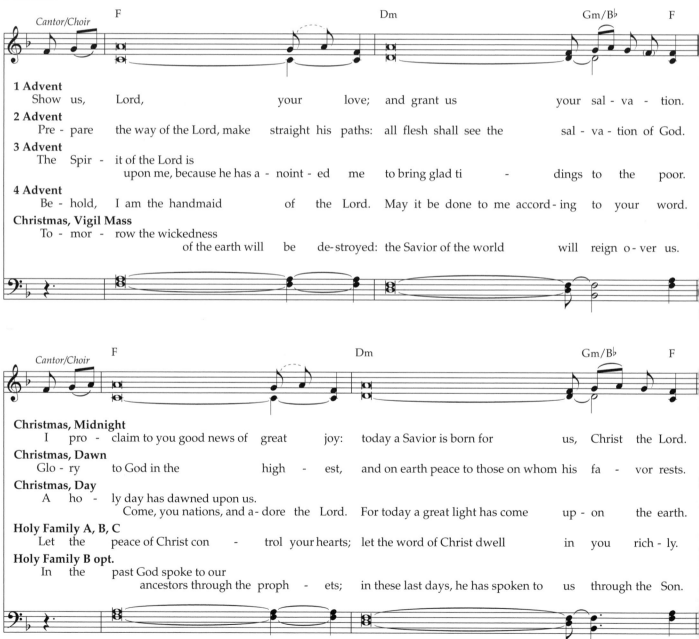

1 Advent
Show us, Lord, your love; and grant us your sal - va - tion.

2 Advent
Pre - pare the way of the Lord, make straight his paths: all flesh shall see the sal - va - tion of God.

3 Advent
The Spir - it of the Lord is upon me, because he has a - noint - ed me to bring glad ti - dings to the poor.

4 Advent
Be - hold, I am the handmaid of the Lord. May it be done to me accord - ing to your word.

Christmas, Vigil Mass
To - mor - row the wickedness of the earth will be de-stroyed: the Savior of the world will reign o - ver us.

Christmas, Midnight
I pro - claim to you good news of great joy: today a Savior is born for us, Christ the Lord.

Christmas, Dawn
Glo - ry to God in the high - est, and on earth peace to those on whom his fa - vor rests.

Christmas, Day
A ho - ly day has dawned upon us. Come, you nations, and a-dore the Lord. For today a great light has come up - on the earth.

Holy Family A, B, C
Let the peace of Christ con - trol your hearts; let the word of Christ dwell in you rich - ly.

Holy Family B opt.
In the past God spoke to our ancestors through the proph - ets; in these last days, he has spoken to us through the Son.

Music © 2000, WLP

Tone 6

Mary, Mother of God
In the past God spoke to our
ancestors through the proph - ets; in these last days, he has spoken to us through the Son.

2 Christmas
Glo - ry to you, O Christ,
proclaimed to the Gen - tiles; Glory to you, O Christ, believed in through-out the world!

Epiphany
We saw his star at its ris - ing and have come to do him hom - age.

Immaculate Conception
Hail, Ma - ry, full of grace, the Lord is with you; blessed are you a - mong wo - men.

Our Lady of Guadalupe
Bless - ed are you, holy Virgin Mary,
deserving of all praise; from you rose the sun of jus - tice, Christ our God.

World Day of Prayer for Peace
Bless - ed are the peace-mak - ers; they shall be called chil - dren of God.

World Day of Prayer for Peace
Peace I leave with you, says the Lord, my peace I give to you.

B150a Gospel Acclamation
Revised

RESPONSE

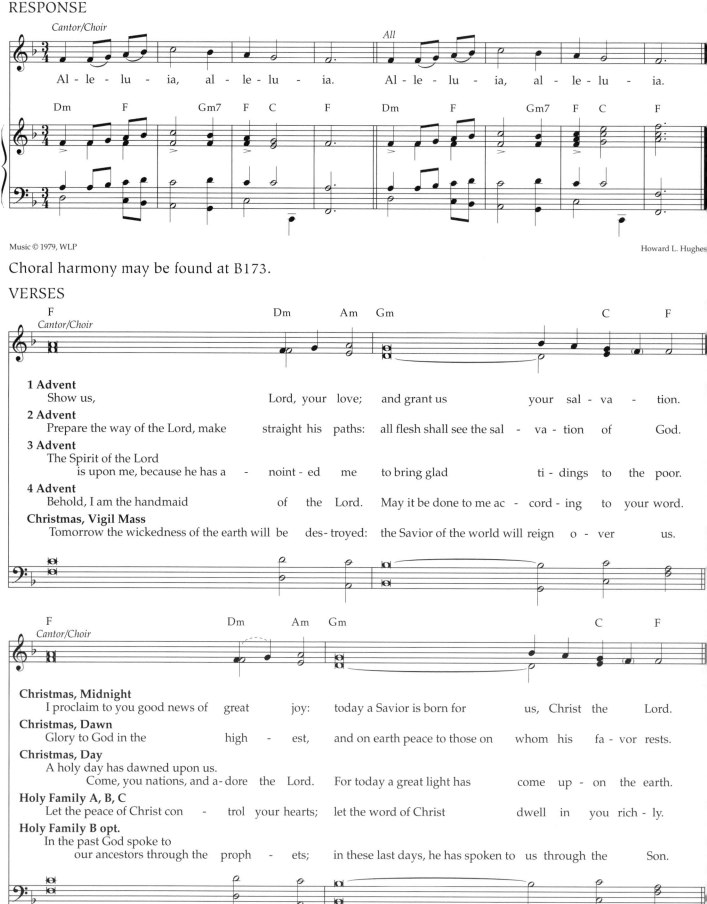

Al - le - lu - ia, al - le - lu - ia. Al - le - lu - ia, al - le - lu - ia.

Music © 1979, WLP

Howard L. Hughes

Choral harmony may be found at B173.

VERSES

1 Advent
Show us, Lord, your love; and grant us your sal - va - tion.

2 Advent
Prepare the way of the Lord, make straight his paths: all flesh shall see the sal - va - tion of God.

3 Advent
The Spirit of the Lord is upon me, because he has a - noint - ed me to bring glad ti - dings to the poor.

4 Advent
Behold, I am the handmaid of the Lord. May it be done to me ac - cord - ing to your word.

Christmas, Vigil Mass
Tomorrow the wickedness of the earth will be des- troyed: the Savior of the world will reign o - ver us.

Christmas, Midnight
I proclaim to you good news of great joy: today a Savior is born for us, Christ the Lord.

Christmas, Dawn
Glory to God in the high - est, and on earth peace to those on whom his fa - vor rests.

Christmas, Day
A holy day has dawned upon us. Come, you nations, and a- dore the Lord. For today a great light has come up - on the earth.

Holy Family A, B, C
Let the peace of Christ con - trol your hearts; let the word of Christ dwell in you rich - ly.

Holy Family B opt.
In the past God spoke to our ancestors through the proph - ets; in these last days, he has spoken to us through the Son.

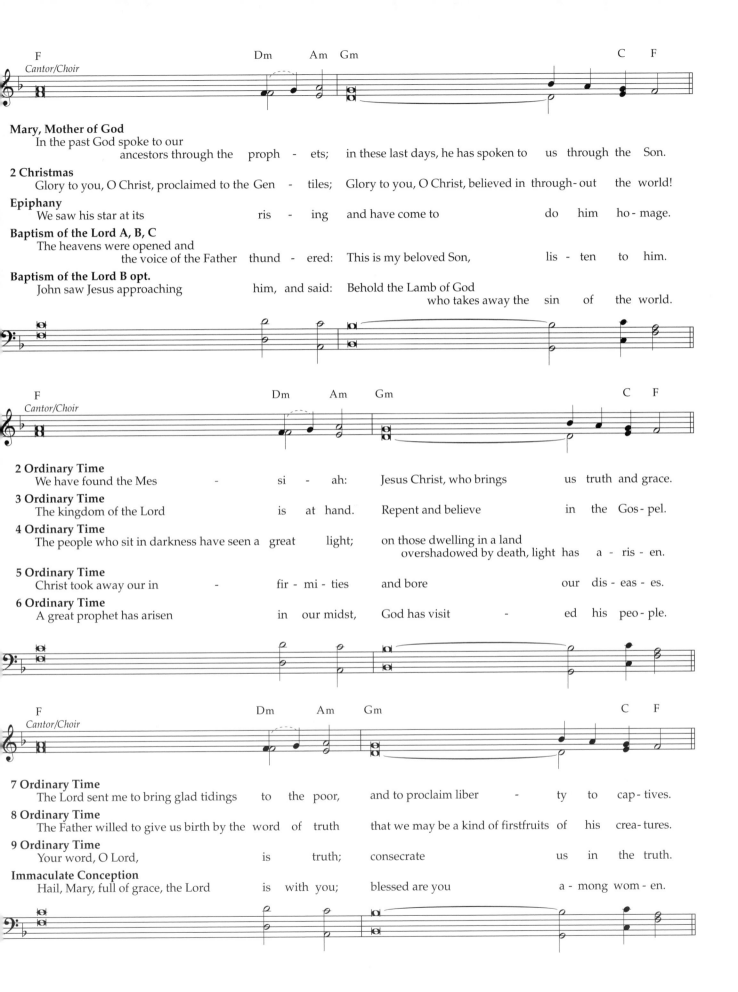

Mary, Mother of God
In the past God spoke to our ancestors through the proph - ets; in these last days, he has spoken to us through the Son.

2 Christmas
Glory to you, O Christ, proclaimed to the Gen - tiles; Glory to you, O Christ, believed in through-out the world!

Epiphany
We saw his star at its ris - ing and have come to do him ho - mage.

Baptism of the Lord A, B, C
The heavens were opened and the voice of the Father thund - ered: This is my beloved Son, lis - ten to him.

Baptism of the Lord B opt.
John saw Jesus approaching him, and said: Behold the Lamb of God who takes away the sin of the world.

2 Ordinary Time
We have found the Mes - si - ah: Jesus Christ, who brings us truth and grace.

3 Ordinary Time
The kingdom of the Lord is at hand. Repent and believe in the Gos - pel.

4 Ordinary Time
The people who sit in darkness have seen a great light; on those dwelling in a land overshadowed by death, light has a - ris - en.

5 Ordinary Time
Christ took away our in - fir - mi - ties and bore our dis - eas - es.

6 Ordinary Time
A great prophet has arisen in our midst, God has visit - ed his peo - ple.

7 Ordinary Time
The Lord sent me to bring glad tidings to the poor, and to proclaim liber - ty to cap - tives.

8 Ordinary Time
The Father willed to give us birth by the word of truth that we may be a kind of firstfruits of his crea - tures.

9 Ordinary Time
Your word, O Lord, is truth; consecrate us in the truth.

Immaculate Conception
Hail, Mary, full of grace, the Lord is with you; blessed are you a - mong wom - en.

B150b Gospel Acclamation

Revised

RESPONSE

Al - le - lu - ia, al - le - lu - ia. Al - le - lu - ia, al - le - lu - ia.

Howard L. Hughes

Choral harmony may be found at B173.

VERSES

Our Lady of Guadalupe
    Blessed are you, holy Virgin Mary,
        deserving of all praise; from you rose the sun of jus - tice, Christ our God.

World Day of Prayer for Peace
    Blessed are the peace - mak - ers; they shall be called chil - dren of God.

World Day of Prayer for Peace
    Peace I leave with you, says the Lord, my peace I give to you.

Presentation of the Lord
    A light of revelation to the Gen - tiles and glory for your peo - ple Is - ra - el.

Howard L. Hughes

RESPONSE

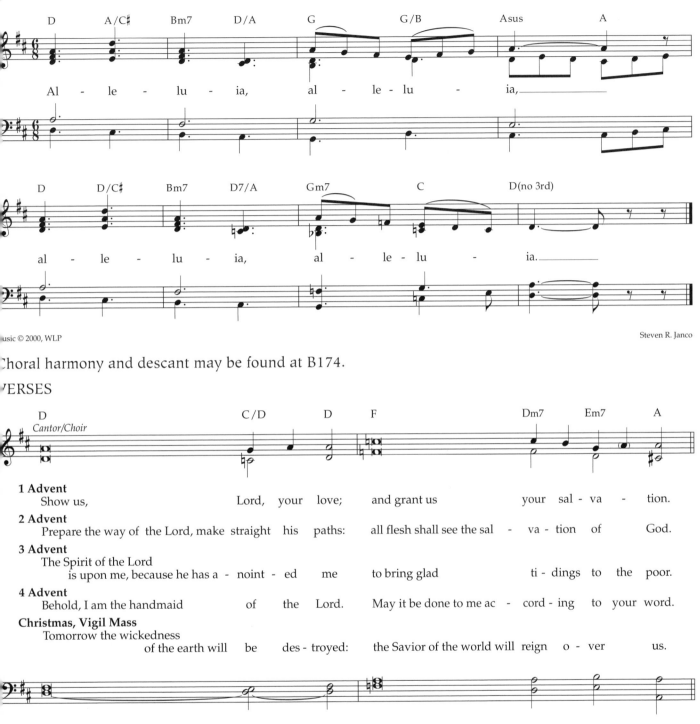

Music © 2000, WLP

Steven R. Janco

Choral harmony and descant may be found at B174.

VERSES

1 Advent
Show us, Lord, your love; and grant us your sal - va - tion.

2 Advent
Prepare the way of the Lord, make straight his paths: all flesh shall see the sal - va - tion of God.

3 Advent
The Spirit of the Lord is upon me, because he has a - noint - ed me to bring glad ti - dings to the poor.

4 Advent
Behold, I am the handmaid of the Lord. May it be done to me ac - cord - ing to your word.

Christmas, Vigil Mass
Tomorrow the wickedness of the earth will be des - troyed: the Savior of the world will reign o - ver us.

Music © 2000, WLP

Steven R. Janco

B151b Gospel Acclamation
Revised
RESPONSE

Music © 2000, WLP

Steven R. Jan[...]

Choral harmony and descant may be found at B174.

VERSES

Cantor/Choir

Christmas, Midnight
I proclaim to you good news of great joy: today a Savior is born for us, Christ the Lord.

Christmas, Dawn
Glory to God in the high - est, and on earth peace to those on whom his fa - vor rests.

Christmas, Day
A holy day has dawned upon us. Come, you nations, and a - dore the Lord. For today a great light has come up - on the earth.

Holy Family A, B, C
Let the peace of Christ con - trol your hearts; let the word of Christ dwell in you rich - ly.

Holy Family B opt.
In the past God spoke to our ancestors through the proph - ets; in these last days, he has spoken to us through the Son.

Music © 2000, WLP

Steven R. Jan[...]

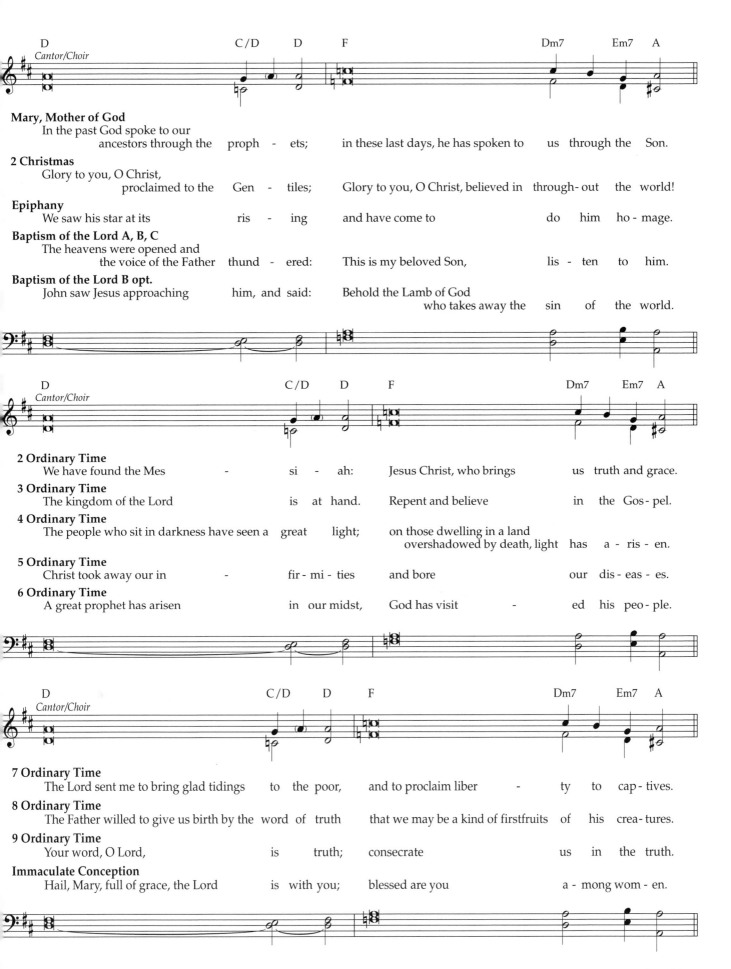

Mary, Mother of God
In the past God spoke to our
ancestors through the proph - ets; in these last days, he has spoken to us through the Son.

2 Christmas
Glory to you, O Christ,
proclaimed to the Gen - tiles; Glory to you, O Christ, believed in through- out the world!

Epiphany
We saw his star at its ris - ing and have come to do him ho - mage.

Baptism of the Lord A, B, C
The heavens were opened and
the voice of the Father thund - ered: This is my beloved Son, lis - ten to him.

Baptism of the Lord B opt.
John saw Jesus approaching him, and said: Behold the Lamb of God
who takes away the sin of the world.

2 Ordinary Time
We have found the Mes - si - ah: Jesus Christ, who brings us truth and grace.

3 Ordinary Time
The kingdom of the Lord is at hand. Repent and believe in the Gos - pel.

4 Ordinary Time
The people who sit in darkness have seen a great light; on those dwelling in a land
overshadowed by death, light has a - ris - en.

5 Ordinary Time
Christ took away our in - fir - mi - ties and bore our dis - eas - es.

6 Ordinary Time
A great prophet has arisen in our midst, God has visit - ed his peo - ple.

7 Ordinary Time
The Lord sent me to bring glad tidings to the poor, and to proclaim liber - ty to cap - tives.

8 Ordinary Time
The Father willed to give us birth by the word of truth that we may be a kind of firstfruits of his crea - tures.

9 Ordinary Time
Your word, O Lord, is truth; consecrate us in the truth.

Immaculate Conception
Hail, Mary, full of grace, the Lord is with you; blessed are you a - mong wom - en.

Steven R. Janco

B151c Gospel Acclamation
Revised

RESPONSE

Music © 2000, WLP

Steven R. Janco

Choral harmony and descant may be found at B174.

VERSES

Our Lady of Guadalupe
Blessed are you, holy Virgin Mary,
deserving of all praise; from you rose the sun of jus - tice, Christ our God.

World Day of Prayer for Peace
Blessed are the peace - mak - ers; they shall be called chil - dren of God.

World Day of Prayer for Peace
Peace I leave with you, says the Lord, my peace I give to you.

Presentation of the Lord
A light of revelation to the Gen - tiles and glory for your peo - ple Is - ra - el.

Music © 2000, WLP

Steven R. Janco

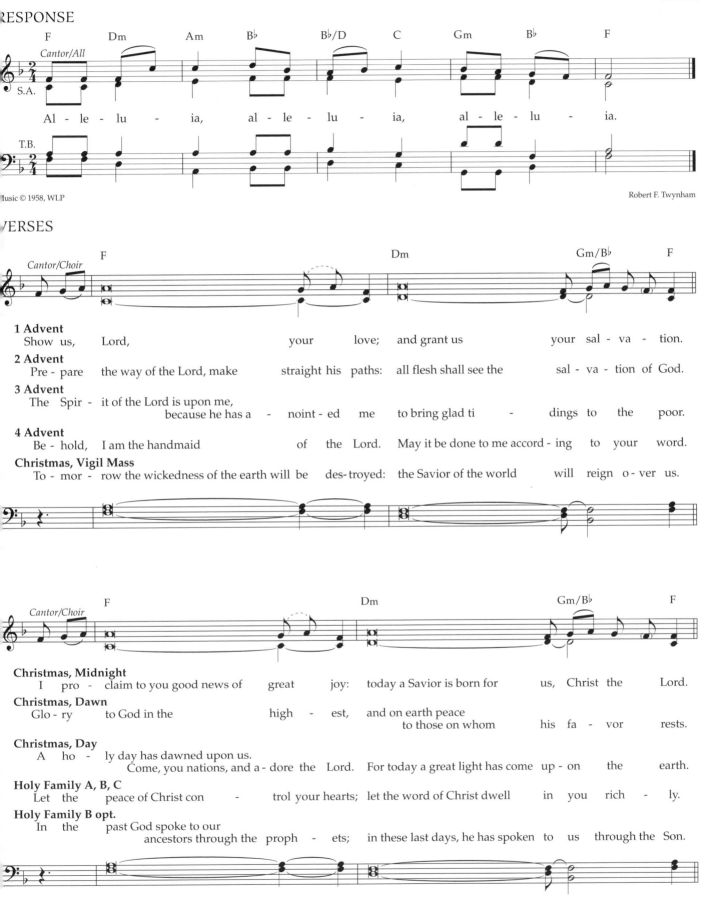

RESPONSE

Cantor/All

Al - le - lu - ia, al - le - lu - ia, al - le - lu - ia.

Music © 1958, WLP

Robert F. Twynham

VERSES

Cantor/Choir

1 Advent
Show us, Lord, your love; and grant us your sal - va - tion.

2 Advent
Pre - pare the way of the Lord, make straight his paths: all flesh shall see the sal - va - tion of God.

3 Advent
The Spir - it of the Lord is upon me, because he has a - noint - ed me to bring glad ti - dings to the poor.

4 Advent
Be - hold, I am the handmaid of the Lord. May it be done to me accord - ing to your word.

Christmas, Vigil Mass
To - mor - row the wickedness of the earth will be des - troyed: the Savior of the world will reign o - ver us.

Cantor/Choir

Christmas, Midnight
I pro - claim to you good news of great joy: today a Savior is born for us, Christ the Lord.

Christmas, Dawn
Glo - ry to God in the high - est, and on earth peace to those on whom his fa - vor rests.

Christmas, Day
A ho - ly day has dawned upon us. Come, you nations, and a - dore the Lord. For today a great light has come up - on the earth.

Holy Family A, B, C
Let the peace of Christ con - trol your hearts; let the word of Christ dwell in you rich - ly.

Holy Family B opt.
In the past God spoke to our ancestors through the proph - ets; in these last days, he has spoken to us through the Son.

Music © 2000, WLP

Tone 6

B152b Gospel Acclamation
Revised

RESPONSE

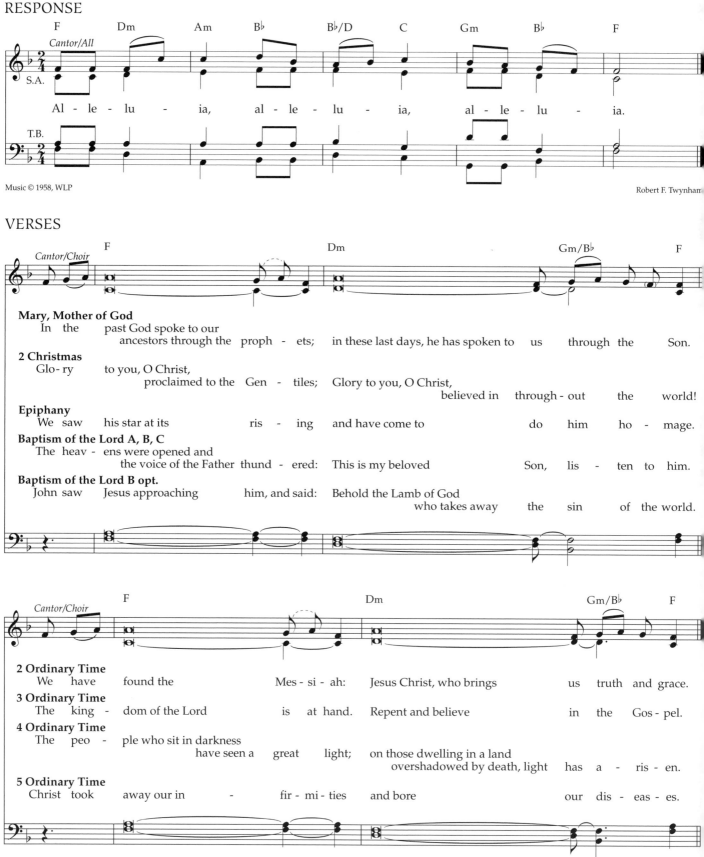

Al - le - lu - ia, al - le - lu - ia, al - le - lu - ia.

Music © 1958, WLP

Robert F. Twynham

VERSES

Mary, Mother of God
In the past God spoke to our ancestors through the proph - ets; in these last days, he has spoken to us through the Son.

2 Christmas
Glo - ry to you, O Christ, proclaimed to the Gen - tiles; Glory to you, O Christ, believed in through - out the world!

Epiphany
We saw his star at its ris - ing and have come to do him ho - mage.

Baptism of the Lord A, B, C
The heav - ens were opened and the voice of the Father thund - ered: This is my beloved Son, lis - ten to him.

Baptism of the Lord B opt.
John saw Jesus approaching him, and said: Behold the Lamb of God who takes away the sin of the world.

2 Ordinary Time
We have found the Mes - si - ah: Jesus Christ, who brings us truth and grace.

3 Ordinary Time
The king - dom of the Lord is at hand. Repent and believe in the Gos - pel.

4 Ordinary Time
The peo - ple who sit in darkness have seen a great light; on those dwelling in a land overshadowed by death, light has a - ris - en.

5 Ordinary Time
Christ took away our in - fir - mi - ties and bore our dis - eas - es.

Music © 2000, WLP

Tone 6

6 Ordinary Time
A great prophet has arisen in our midst, God has visited his people.

7 Ordinary Time
The Lord sent me to bring glad tidings to the poor, and to proclaim liberty to captives.

8 Ordinary Time
The Father willed to give us birth by the word of truth that we may be a kind of firstfruits of his creatures.

9 Ordinary Time
Your word, O Lord, is truth; consecrate us in the truth.

Immaculate Conception
Hail, Mary, full of grace, the Lord is with you; blessed are you among women.

Our Lady of Guadalupe
Blessed are you, holy Virgin Mary, deserving of all praise; from you rose the sun of justice, Christ our God.

World Day of Prayer for Peace
Blessed are the peacemakers; they shall be called children of God.

World Day of Prayer for Peace
Peace I leave with you, says the Lord, my peace I give to you.

Presentation of the Lord
A light of revelation to the Gentiles and glory for your people Israel.

B153 Lenten Gospel Acclamation
Revised

RESPONSE

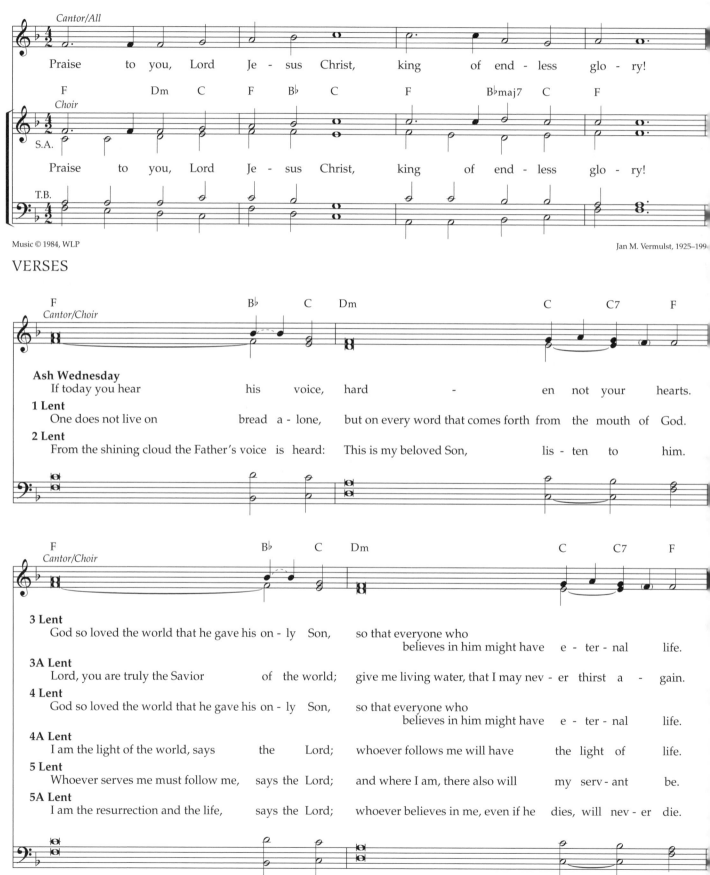

Cantor/All

Praise to you, Lord Je - sus Christ, king of end - less glo - ry!

Choir

Praise to you, Lord Je - sus Christ, king of end - less glo - ry!

Music © 1984, WLP

Jan M. Vermulst, 1925–199[

VERSES

Ash Wednesday
If today you hear his voice, hard - en not your hearts.

1 Lent
One does not live on bread a - lone, but on every word that comes forth from the mouth of God.

2 Lent
From the shining cloud the Father's voice is heard: This is my beloved Son, lis - ten to him.

3 Lent
God so loved the world that he gave his on - ly Son, so that everyone who believes in him might have e - ter - nal life.

3A Lent
Lord, you are truly the Savior of the world; give me living water, that I may nev - er thirst a - gain.

4 Lent
God so loved the world that he gave his on - ly Son, so that everyone who believes in him might have e - ter - nal life.

4A Lent
I am the light of the world, says the Lord; whoever follows me will have the light of life.

5 Lent
Whoever serves me must follow me, says the Lord; and where I am, there also will my serv - ant be.

5A Lent
I am the resurrection and the life, says the Lord; whoever believes in me, even if he dies, will nev - er die.

Music © 1984, WLP

Jan M. Vermulst, 1925–1994

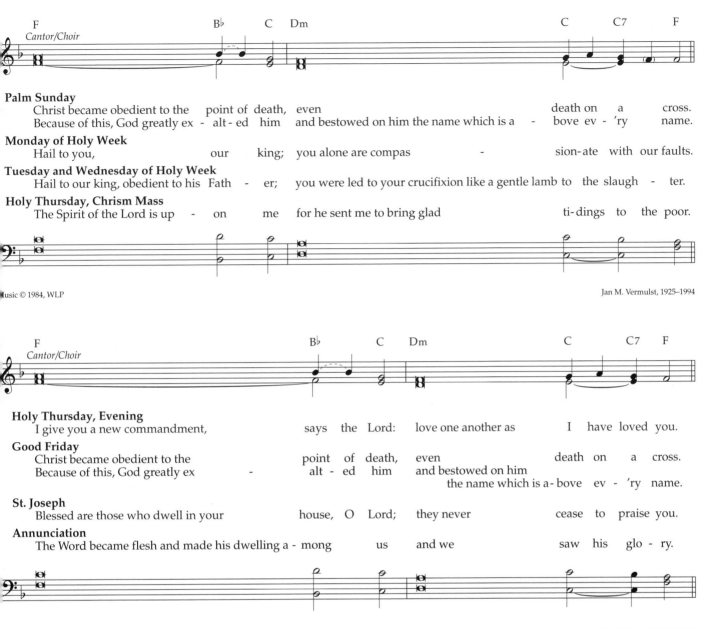

Palm Sunday
Christ became obedient to the point of death, even death on a cross.
Because of this, God greatly ex - alt - ed him and bestowed on him the name which is a - bove ev - 'ry name.

Monday of Holy Week
Hail to you, our king; you alone are compas - sion-ate with our faults.

Tuesday and Wednesday of Holy Week
Hail to our king, obedient to his Fath - er; you were led to your crucifixion like a gentle lamb to the slaugh - ter.

Holy Thursday, Chrism Mass
The Spirit of the Lord is up - on me for he sent me to bring glad ti-dings to the poor.

Music © 1984, WLP

Jan M. Vermulst, 1925–1994

Holy Thursday, Evening
I give you a new commandment, says the Lord: love one another as I have loved you.

Good Friday
Christ became obedient to the point of death, even death on a cross.
Because of this, God greatly ex - alt - ed him and bestowed on him the name which is a-bove ev - 'ry name.

St. Joseph
Blessed are those who dwell in your house, O Lord; they never cease to praise you.

Annunciation
The Word became flesh and made his dwelling a - mong us and we saw his glo - ry.

Music © 1984, WLP

Jan M. Vermulst, 1925–1994

B154 Lenten Gospel Acclamation

Revised

RESPONSE

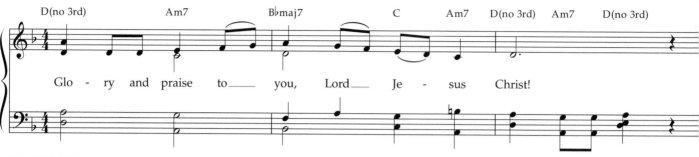

Glo - ry and praise to____ you, Lord____ Je - sus Christ!

Steven R. Jan

Choral harmony and descant may be found at B184.

VERSES

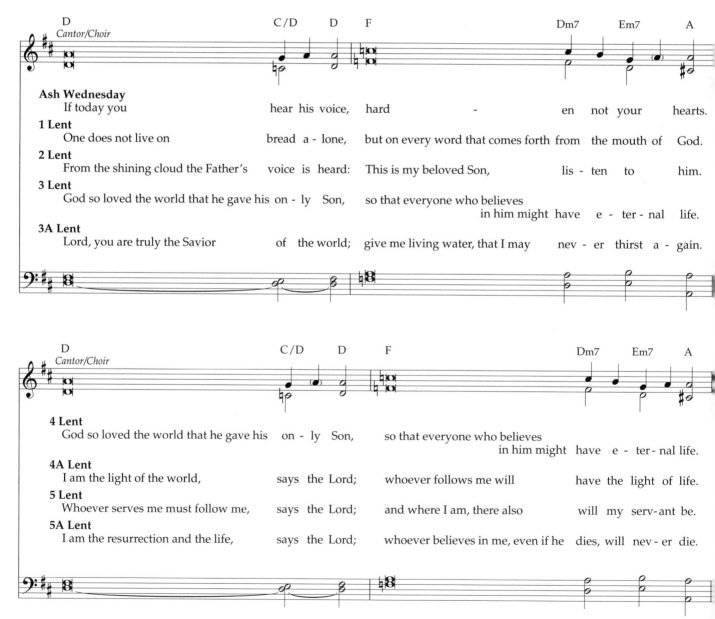

Ash Wednesday
If today you   hear his voice, hard - en not your hearts.

1 Lent
One does not live on   bread a - lone, but on every word that comes forth from the mouth of God.

2 Lent
From the shining cloud the Father's   voice is heard: This is my beloved Son, lis - ten to him.

3 Lent
God so loved the world that he gave his on - ly Son, so that everyone who believes in him might have e - ter - nal life.

3A Lent
Lord, you are truly the Savior   of the world; give me living water, that I may nev - er thirst a - gain.

4 Lent
God so loved the world that he gave his on - ly Son, so that everyone who believes in him might have e - ter - nal life.

4A Lent
I am the light of the world,   says the Lord; whoever follows me will have the light of life.

5 Lent
Whoever serves me must follow me,   says the Lord; and where I am, there also will my serv-ant be.

5A Lent
I am the resurrection and the life,   says the Lord; whoever believes in me, even if he dies, will nev - er die.

Steven R. Janco

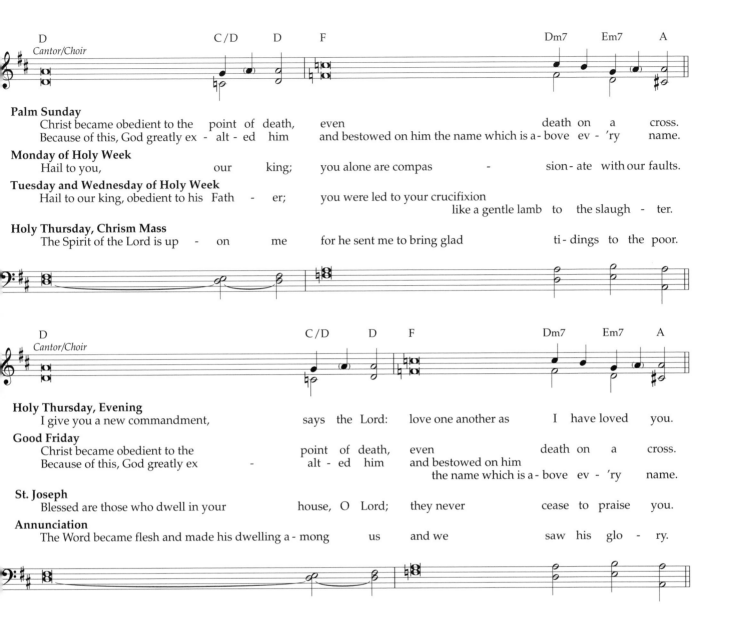

Palm Sunday
Christ became obedient to the   point of death,   even   death on   a   cross.
Because of this, God greatly ex - alt - ed   him   and bestowed on him the name which is a- bove   ev - 'ry   name.

Monday of Holy Week
Hail to you,   our   king;   you alone are compas   -   sion- ate   with our faults.

Tuesday and Wednesday of Holy Week
Hail to our king, obedient to his   Fath   -   er;   you were led to your crucifixion
like a gentle lamb   to   the slaugh - ter.

Holy Thursday, Chrism Mass
The Spirit of the Lord is up   -   on   me   for he sent me to bring glad   ti- dings   to   the poor.

Holy Thursday, Evening
I give you a new commandment,   says   the   Lord: love one another as   I   have loved   you.

Good Friday
Christ became obedient to the   point   of   death,   even   death on   a   cross.
Because of this, God greatly ex   -   alt - ed   him   and bestowed on him
the name which is a - bove   ev - 'ry   name.

St. Joseph
Blessed are those who dwell in your   house, O   Lord;   they never   cease   to   praise   you.

Annunciation
The Word became flesh and made his dwelling a - mong   us   and we   saw   his   glo   -   ry.

B155 Lenten Gospel Acclamation
Revised

RESPONSE

Praise and hon - or to you, Lord Je - sus Christ!

Praise and hon - or to you, Lord Je - sus Christ!

Paul M. French

VERSES

Ash Wednesday
If today you hear his voice, hard - en not your hearts.

1 Lent
One does not live on bread a - lone, but on every word that comes forth from the mouth of God.

2 Lent
From the shining cloud the Father's voice is heard: This is my beloved Son, lis - ten to him.

Paul M. French

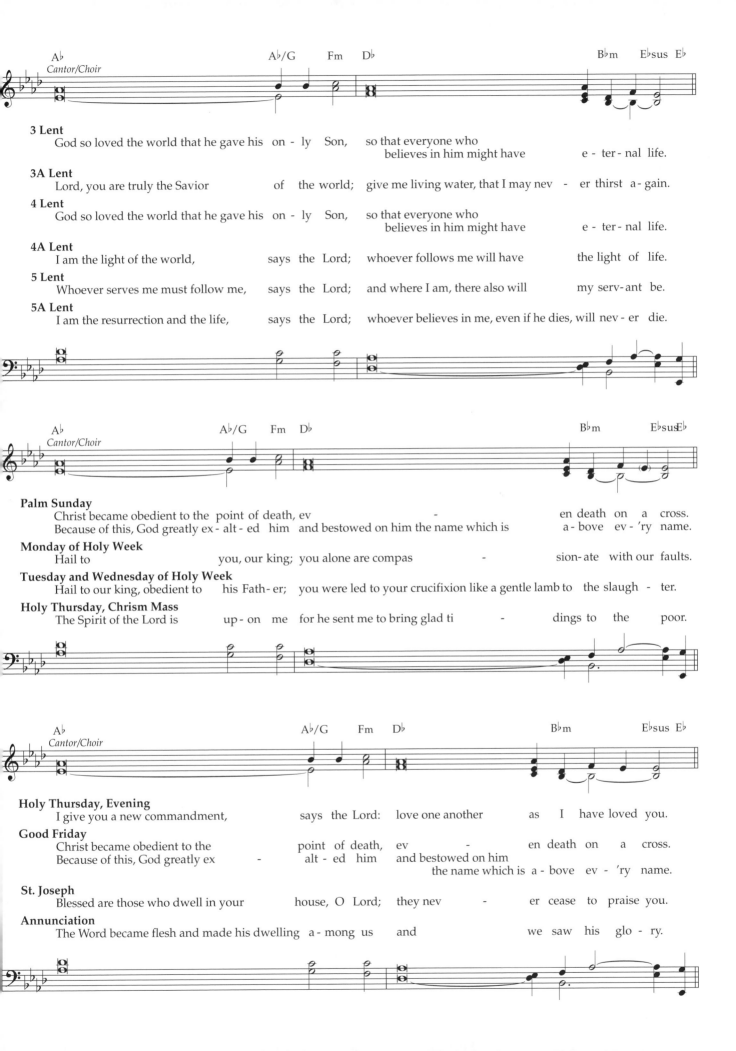

3 Lent
God so loved the world that he gave his on - ly Son, so that everyone who believes in him might have e - ter - nal life.

3A Lent
Lord, you are truly the Savior of the world; give me living water, that I may nev - er thirst a - gain.

4 Lent
God so loved the world that he gave his on - ly Son, so that everyone who believes in him might have e - ter - nal life.

4A Lent
I am the light of the world, says the Lord; whoever follows me will have the light of life.

5 Lent
Whoever serves me must follow me, says the Lord; and where I am, there also will my serv-ant be.

5A Lent
I am the resurrection and the life, says the Lord; whoever believes in me, even if he dies, will nev - er die.

Palm Sunday
Christ became obedient to the point of death, ev - en death on a cross.
Because of this, God greatly ex - alt - ed him and bestowed on him the name which is a - bove ev - 'ry name.

Monday of Holy Week
Hail to you, our king; you alone are compas - sion-ate with our faults.

Tuesday and Wednesday of Holy Week
Hail to our king, obedient to his Fath-er; you were led to your crucifixion like a gentle lamb to the slaugh - ter.

Holy Thursday, Chrism Mass
The Spirit of the Lord is up - on me for he sent me to bring glad ti - dings to the poor.

Holy Thursday, Evening
I give you a new commandment, says the Lord: love one another as I have loved you.

Good Friday
Christ became obedient to the point of death, ev - en death on a cross.
Because of this, God greatly ex - alt - ed him and bestowed on him the name which is a - bove ev - 'ry name.

St. Joseph
Blessed are those who dwell in your house, O Lord; they nev - er cease to praise you.

Annunciation
The Word became flesh and made his dwelling a - mong us and we saw his glo - ry.

B156 Lenten Gospel Acclamation

Revised

RESPONSE

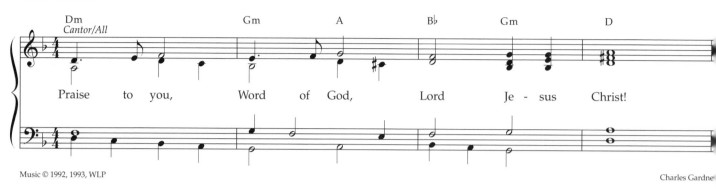

Praise to you, Word of God, Lord Je-sus Christ!

Music © 1992, 1993, WLP

Charles Gardner

Choral harmony may be found at B185.

VERSES

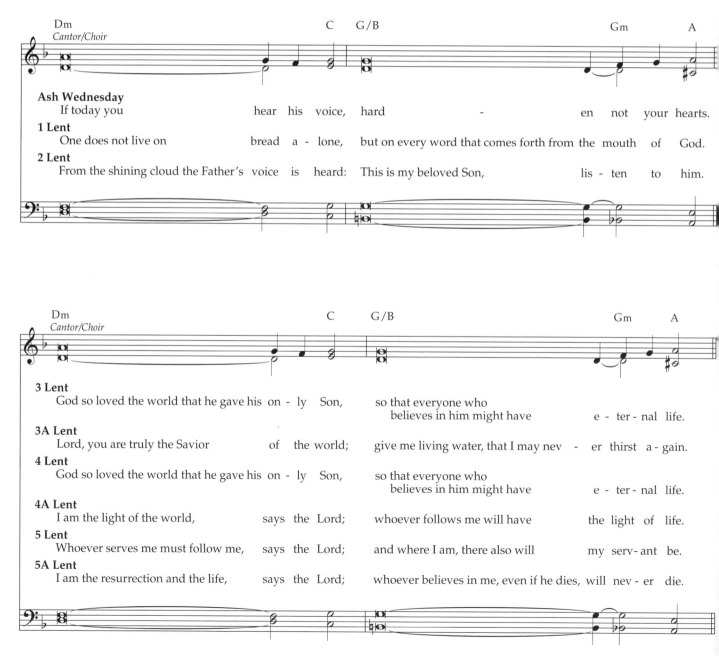

Ash Wednesday
If today you hear his voice, hard - en not your hearts.

1 Lent
One does not live on bread a - lone, but on every word that comes forth from the mouth of God.

2 Lent
From the shining cloud the Father's voice is heard: This is my beloved Son, lis - ten to him.

3 Lent
God so loved the world that he gave his on - ly Son, so that everyone who believes in him might have e - ter - nal life.

3A Lent
Lord, you are truly the Savior of the world; give me living water, that I may nev - er thirst a - gain.

4 Lent
God so loved the world that he gave his on - ly Son, so that everyone who believes in him might have e - ter - nal life.

4A Lent
I am the light of the world, says the Lord; whoever follows me will have the light of life.

5 Lent
Whoever serves me must follow me, says the Lord; and where I am, there also will my serv-ant be.

5A Lent
I am the resurrection and the life, says the Lord; whoever believes in me, even if he dies, will nev - er die.

Music © 1992, 1993, WLP

Charles Gardner

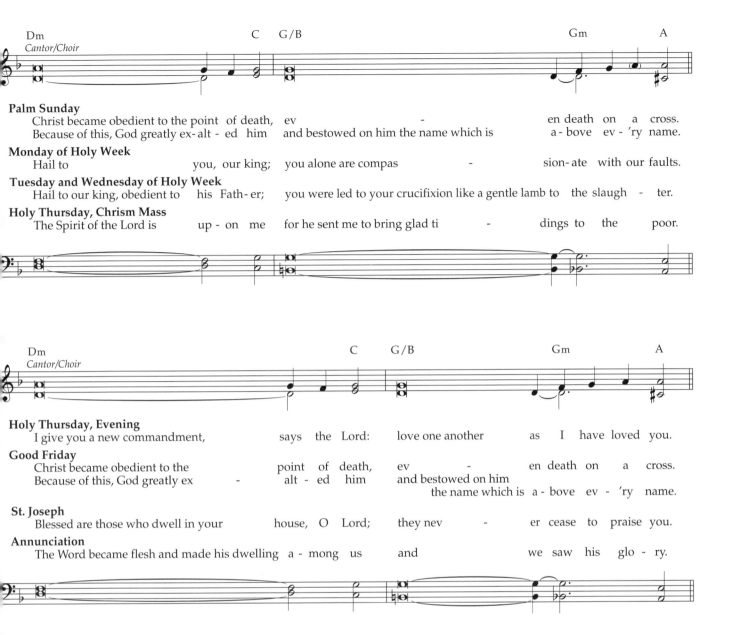

Palm Sunday
Christ became obedient to the point of death, ev - en death on a cross.
Because of this, God greatly ex- alt - ed him and bestowed on him the name which is a - bove ev - 'ry name.

Monday of Holy Week
Hail to you, our king; you alone are compas - sion- ate with our faults.

Tuesday and Wednesday of Holy Week
Hail to our king, obedient to his Fath- er; you were led to your crucifixion like a gentle lamb to the slaugh - ter.

Holy Thursday, Chrism Mass
The Spirit of the Lord is up - on me for he sent me to bring glad ti - dings to the poor.

Holy Thursday, Evening
I give you a new commandment, says the Lord: love one another as I have loved you.

Good Friday
Christ became obedient to the point of death, ev - en death on a cross.
Because of this, God greatly ex - alt - ed him and bestowed on him the name which is a - bove ev - 'ry name.

St. Joseph
Blessed are those who dwell in your house, O Lord; they nev - er cease to praise you.

Annunciation
The Word became flesh and made his dwelling a - mong us and we saw his glo - ry.

B157 Gospel Acclamation
Revised

RESPONSE

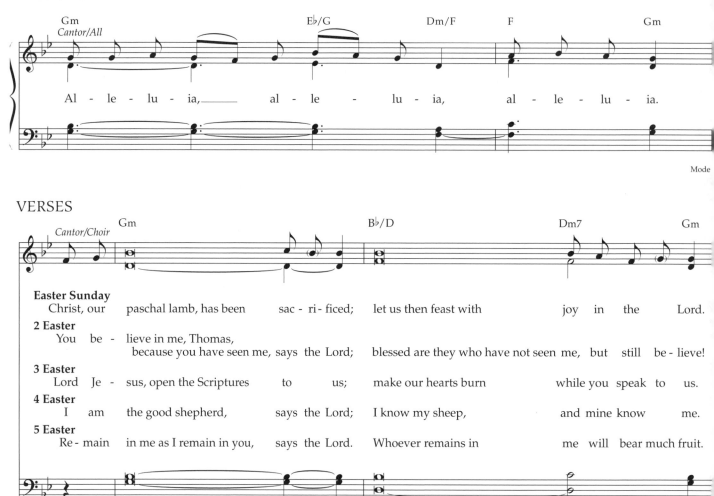

Al - le - lu - ia, ___ al - le - lu - ia, al - le - lu - ia.

Mode

VERSES

Easter Sunday
Christ, our paschal lamb, has been sac - ri - ficed; let us then feast with joy in the Lord.

2 Easter
You be - lieve in me, Thomas,
because you have seen me, says the Lord; blessed are they who have not seen me, but still be - lieve!

3 Easter
Lord Je - sus, open the Scriptures to us; make our hearts burn while you speak to us.

4 Easter
I am the good shepherd, says the Lord; I know my sheep, and mine know me.

5 Easter
Re - main in me as I remain in you, says the Lord. Whoever remains in me will bear much fruit.

Tone

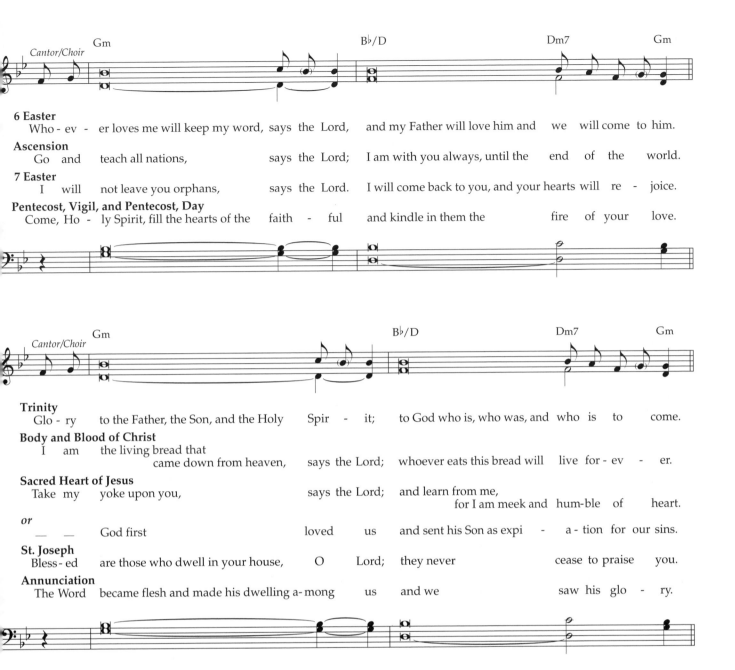

6 Easter
Who - ev - er loves me will keep my word, says the Lord, and my Father will love him and we will come to him.

Ascension
Go and teach all nations, says the Lord; I am with you always, until the end of the world.

7 Easter
I will not leave you orphans, says the Lord. I will come back to you, and your hearts will re - joice.

Pentecost, Vigil, and Pentecost, Day
Come, Ho - ly Spirit, fill the hearts of the faith - ful and kindle in them the fire of your love.

Trinity
Glo - ry to the Father, the Son, and the Holy Spir - it; to God who is, who was, and who is to come.

Body and Blood of Christ
I am the living bread that came down from heaven, says the Lord; whoever eats this bread will live for - ev - er.

Sacred Heart of Jesus
Take my yoke upon you, says the Lord; and learn from me, for I am meek and hum-ble of heart.

or
— — God first loved us and sent his Son as expi - a - tion for our sins.

St. Joseph
Bless - ed are those who dwell in your house, O Lord; they never cease to praise you.

Annunciation
The Word became flesh and made his dwelling a- mong us and we saw his glo - ry.

B158 Gospel Acclamation
Revised

RESPONSE

Al - le - lu - ia, al - le - lu - ia, al - le - lu - ia.

Music © 1971, WLP

James O. Gerris

VERSES

Easter Sunday
Christ, our   paschal lamb, has been   sac - ri - ficed; let us then feast with   joy   in   the   Lord.

2 Easter
You   be - lieve in me, Thomas,
        because you have seen me, says the Lord; blessed are they who have not seen me, but   still   be - lieve!

3 Easter
Lord   Je - sus, open the Scriptures   to   us;   make our hearts burn   while you speak to   us.

4 Easter
I   am   the good shepherd,   says the Lord; I know my sheep,   and mine know   me.

5 Easter
Re - main   in me as I remain in you,   says the Lord. Whoever remains in   me   will bear much fruit.

Music © 2000, WLP

Tone 8

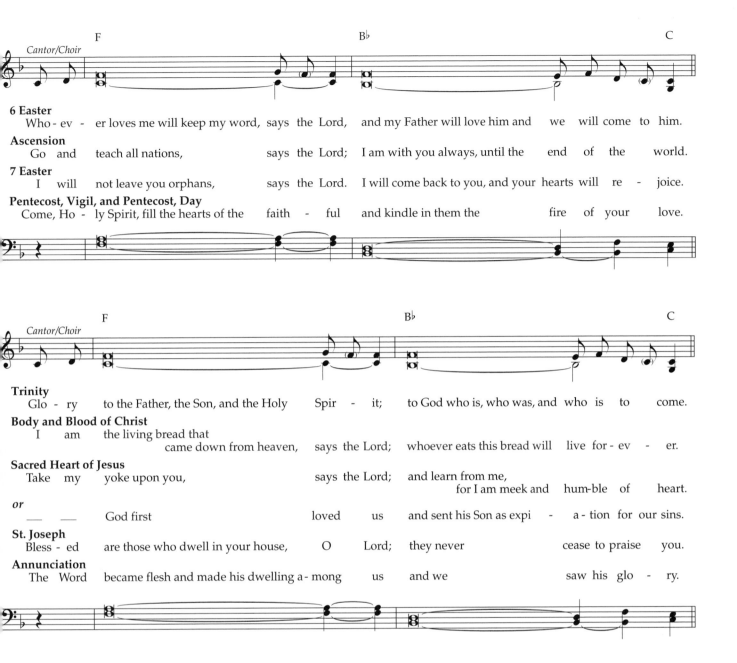

6 Easter
Who - ev - er loves me will keep my word, says the Lord, and my Father will love him and we will come to him.

Ascension
Go and teach all nations, says the Lord; I am with you always, until the end of the world.

7 Easter
I will not leave you orphans, says the Lord. I will come back to you, and your hearts will re - joice.

Pentecost, Vigil, and Pentecost, Day
Come, Ho - ly Spirit, fill the hearts of the faith - ful and kindle in them the fire of your love.

Trinity
Glo - ry to the Father, the Son, and the Holy Spir - it; to God who is, who was, and who is to come.

Body and Blood of Christ
I am the living bread that came down from heaven, says the Lord; whoever eats this bread will live for - ev - er.

Sacred Heart of Jesus
Take my yoke upon you, says the Lord; and learn from me, for I am meek and hum-ble of heart.

or
___ ___ God first loved us and sent his Son as expi - a - tion for our sins.

St. Joseph
Bless - ed are those who dwell in your house, O Lord; they never cease to praise you.

Annunciation
The Word became flesh and made his dwelling a - mong us and we saw his glo - ry.

B159 Gospel Acclamation

Revised

RESPONSE

Al - le - lu - ia, al - le - lu - ia, al - le - lu - ia.

Al - le - lu - ia, al - le - lu - ia, al - le - lu - ia.

Music © 1996, WLP

Steven R. Janc

VERSES

Cantor/Choir

Easter Sunday
Christ, our   paschal lamb, has been   sac - ri - ficed;   let us then feast with   joy   in   the   Lord.

2 Easter
You   be - lieve in me, Thomas,
because you have seen me, says the Lord;   blessed are they who have not seen   me,   but   still   be - lieve!

3 Easter
Lord   Je - sus, open the Scriptures   to   us;   make our hearts burn   while you speak   to   us.

4 Easter
I   am   the good shepherd,   says the Lord;   I know my sheep,   and mine know   me.

5 Easter
Re - main   in me as I remain in you,   says the Lord.   Whoever remains in   me   will   bear much fruit.

Music © 1984, WLP

Robert E. Kreutz, 1922–1996

D   Bm   F♯m7   Bm   Em   Em7   A7   D

Cantor/Choir

6 Easter
Who - ev - er loves me will keep my word, says the Lord, and my Father will love him and we will come to him.

Ascension
Go and teach all nations, says the Lord; I am with you always, until the end of the world.

7 Easter
I will not leave you orphans, says the Lord. I will come back to you, and your hearts will re - joice.

Pentecost, Vigil, and Pentecost, Day
Come, Ho - ly Spirit, fill the hearts of the faith - ful and kindle in them the fire of your love.

D   Bm   F♯m7   Bm   Em   Em7   A7   D

Cantor/Choir

Trinity
Glo - ry to the Father, the Son, and the Holy Spir - it; to God who is, who was, and who is to come.

Body and Blood of Christ
I am the living bread that came down from heaven, says the Lord; whoever eats this bread will live for - ev - er.

Sacred Heart of Jesus
Take my yoke upon you, says the Lord; and learn from me, for I am meek and hum - ble of heart.

or
_ _ God first loved us and sent his Son as expi - a - tion for our sins.

St. Joseph
Bless - ed are those who dwell in your house, O Lord; they never cease to praise you.

Annunciation
The Word became flesh and made his dwelling a - mong us and we saw his glo - ry.

B160a   Gospel Acclamation

Revised

RESPONSE

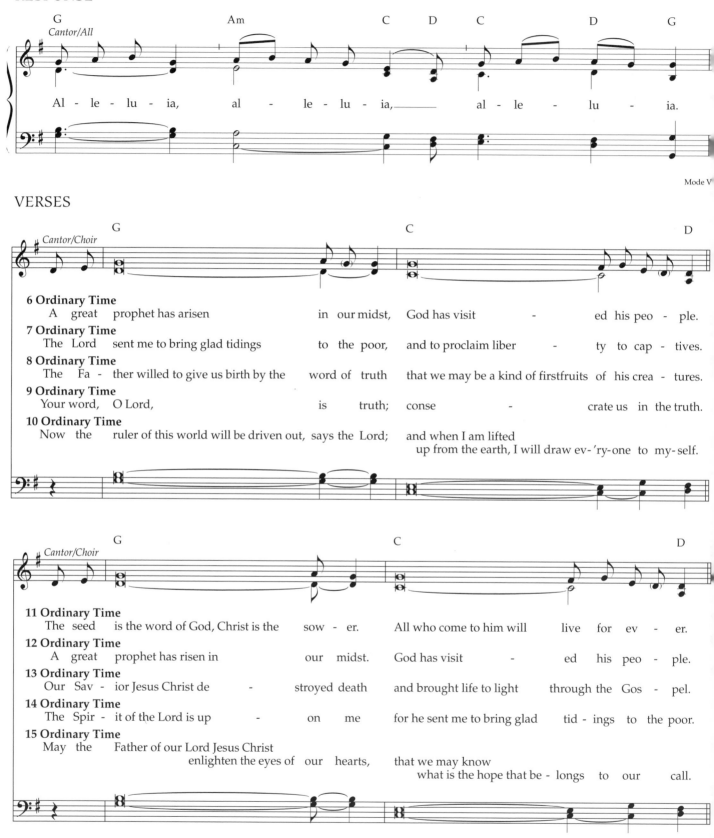

Al - le - lu - ia,   al - le - lu - ia,____ al - le - lu - ia.

Mode V

VERSES

6 Ordinary Time
A   great   prophet has arisen   in   our midst,   God has visit - ed his peo - ple.

7 Ordinary Time
The   Lord   sent me to bring glad tidings   to   the poor,   and to proclaim liber - ty to cap - tives.

8 Ordinary Time
The   Fa - ther willed to give us birth by the   word of truth   that we may be a kind of firstfruits of his crea - tures.

9 Ordinary Time
Your word,   O Lord,   is   truth;   conse - crate us in the truth.

10 Ordinary Time
Now   the   ruler of this world will be driven out, says the Lord;   and when I am lifted
up from the earth, I will draw ev-'ry-one to my-self.

11 Ordinary Time
The   seed   is the word of God, Christ is the   sow - er.   All who come to him will   live   for   ev - er.

12 Ordinary Time
A   great   prophet has risen in   our midst.   God has visit - ed   his peo - ple.

13 Ordinary Time
Our   Sav - ior Jesus Christ de - stroyed death   and brought life to light   through the Gos - pel.

14 Ordinary Time
The   Spir - it of the Lord is up - on   me   for he sent me to bring glad   tid - ings to the poor.

15 Ordinary Time
May   the   Father of our Lord Jesus Christ
enlighten the eyes of our   hearts,   that we may know
what is the hope that be - longs   to   our   call.

Tone 8G

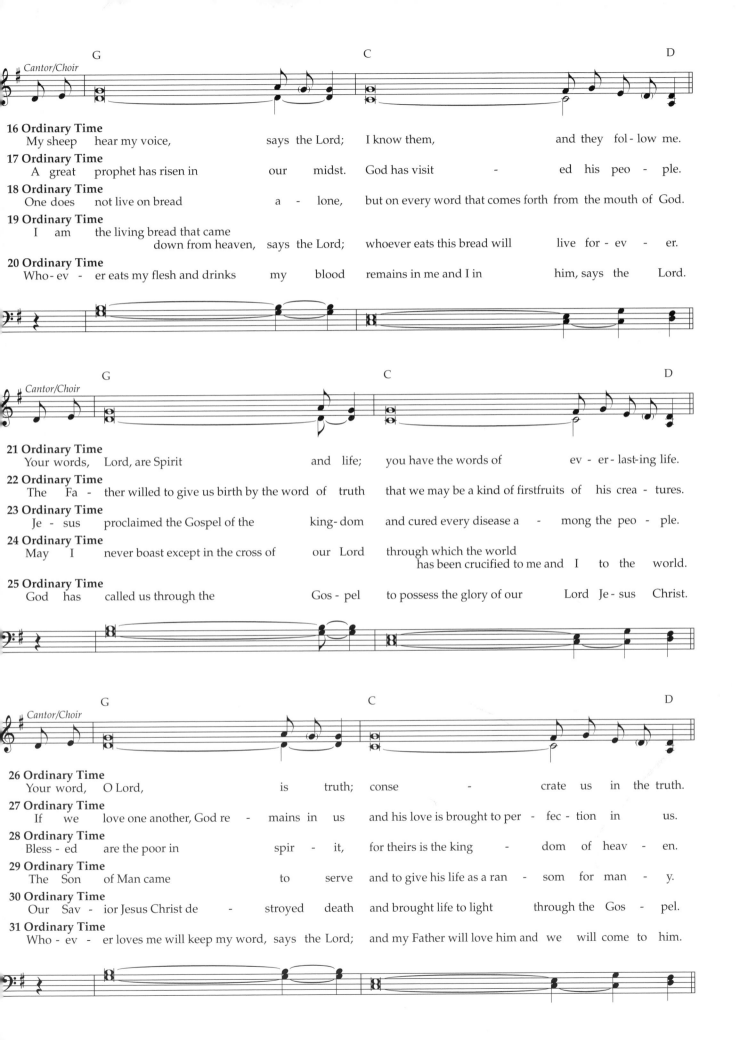

16 Ordinary Time
My sheep hear my voice, says the Lord; I know them, and they fol-low me.

17 Ordinary Time
A great prophet has risen in our midst. God has visit - ed his peo - ple.

18 Ordinary Time
One does not live on bread a - lone, but on every word that comes forth from the mouth of God.

19 Ordinary Time
I am the living bread that came down from heaven, says the Lord; whoever eats this bread will live for - ev - er.

20 Ordinary Time
Who-ev - er eats my flesh and drinks my blood remains in me and I in him, says the Lord.

21 Ordinary Time
Your words, Lord, are Spirit and life; you have the words of ev - er - last-ing life.

22 Ordinary Time
The Fa - ther willed to give us birth by the word of truth that we may be a kind of firstfruits of his crea - tures.

23 Ordinary Time
Je - sus proclaimed the Gospel of the king-dom and cured every disease a - mong the peo - ple.

24 Ordinary Time
May I never boast except in the cross of our Lord through which the world has been crucified to me and I to the world.

25 Ordinary Time
God has called us through the Gos - pel to possess the glory of our Lord Je - sus Christ.

26 Ordinary Time
Your word, O Lord, is truth; conse - crate us in the truth.

27 Ordinary Time
If we love one another, God re - mains in us and his love is brought to per - fec - tion in us.

28 Ordinary Time
Bless - ed are the poor in spir - it, for theirs is the king - dom of heav - en.

29 Ordinary Time
The Son of Man came to serve and to give his life as a ran - som for man - y.

30 Ordinary Time
Our Sav - ior Jesus Christ de - stroyed death and brought life to light through the Gos - pel.

31 Ordinary Time
Who - ev - er loves me will keep my word, says the Lord; and my Father will love him and we will come to him.

B160b Gospel Acclamation
Revised

RESPONSE

VERSES

Mode V

32 Ordinary Time
Bless - ed are the poor in spir - it, for theirs is the king - dom of heav - en.

33 Ordinary Time
Be vig - ilant at all times and pray that you have the strength to stand be - fore the Son of Man.

Christ the King
Bless - ed is he who comes in the name of the Lord! Blessed is the kingdom of our father Dav - id that is to come!

Nativity of St. John the Baptist, Vigil
He came to testify to the light, to prepare a people fit for the Lord.

Nativity of St. John the Baptist, during the Day
You, child, will be called prophet of the Most High, for you will go before the Lord to pre - pare his way.

Tone 8

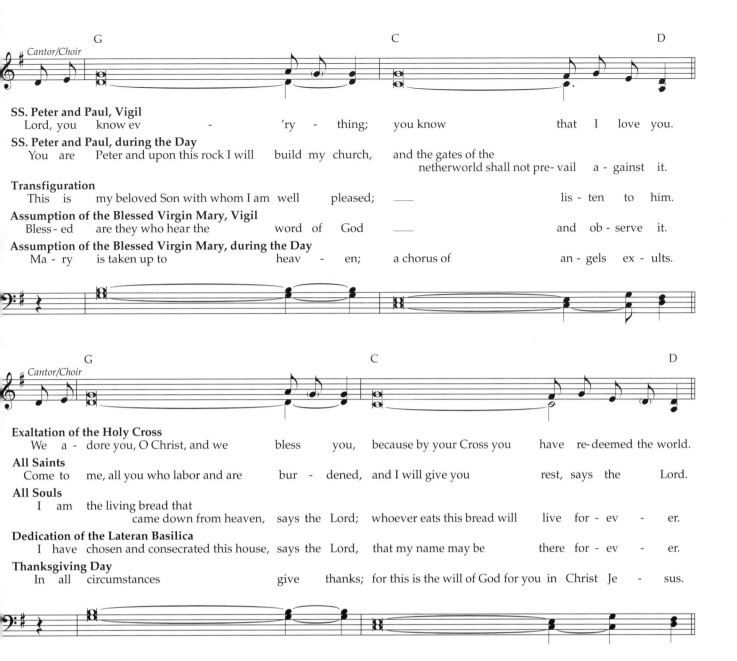

SS. Peter and Paul, Vigil
Lord, you know ev - 'ry - thing; you know that I love you.

SS. Peter and Paul, during the Day
You are Peter and upon this rock I will build my church, and the gates of the netherworld shall not pre - vail a - gainst it.

Transfiguration
This is my beloved Son with whom I am well pleased; ___ lis - ten to him.

Assumption of the Blessed Virgin Mary, Vigil
Bless - ed are they who hear the word of God ___ and ob - serve it.

Assumption of the Blessed Virgin Mary, during the Day
Ma - ry is taken up to heav - en; a chorus of an - gels ex - ults.

Exaltation of the Holy Cross
We a - dore you, O Christ, and we bless you, because by your Cross you have re - deemed the world.

All Saints
Come to me, all you who labor and are bur - dened, and I will give you rest, says the Lord.

All Souls
I am the living bread that came down from heaven, says the Lord; whoever eats this bread will live for - ev - er.

Dedication of the Lateran Basilica
I have chosen and consecrated this house, says the Lord, that my name may be there for - ev - er.

Thanksgiving Day
In all circumstances give thanks; for this is the will of God for you in Christ Je - sus.

B161a   Gospel Acclamation
Revised

RESPONSE

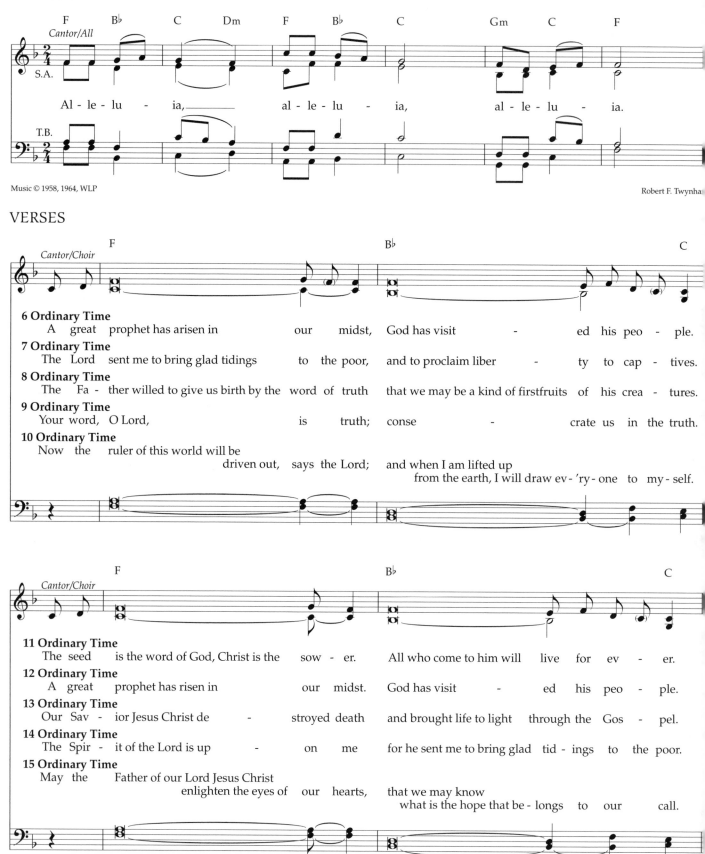

Music © 1958, 1964, WLP

Robert F. Twynha[m]

VERSES

6 Ordinary Time
A   great   prophet has arisen in   our   midst, God has visit - ed his peo - ple.

7 Ordinary Time
The   Lord   sent me to bring glad tidings   to   the poor, and to proclaim liber - ty to cap - tives.

8 Ordinary Time
The   Fa - ther willed to give us birth by the   word   of truth   that we may be a kind of firstfruits of his crea - tures.

9 Ordinary Time
Your word, O Lord,   is   truth;   conse - crate us   in the truth.

10 Ordinary Time
Now   the   ruler of this world will be   driven out,   says the Lord;   and when I am lifted up   from the earth, I will draw ev - 'ry - one   to   my - self.

11 Ordinary Time
The   seed   is the word of God, Christ is the   sow - er.   All who come to him will   live   for   ev - er.

12 Ordinary Time
A   great   prophet has risen in   our   midst.   God has visit - ed   his   peo - ple.

13 Ordinary Time
Our   Sav - ior Jesus Christ de - stroyed death   and brought life to light   through the   Gos - pel.

14 Ordinary Time
The   Spir - it of the Lord is up - on   me   for he sent me to bring glad   tid - ings   to   the poor.

15 Ordinary Time
May   the   Father of our Lord Jesus Christ   enlighten the eyes of   our   hearts,   that we may know   what is the hope that be - longs   to   our   call.

Music © 2000, WLP

Tone 8[C]

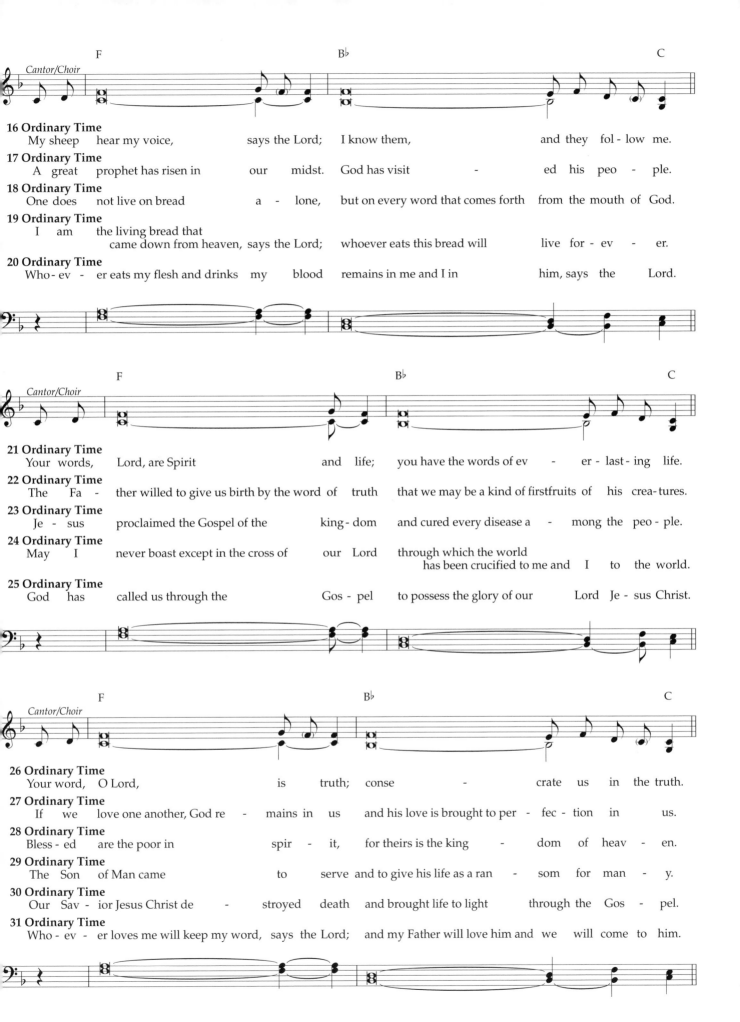

16 Ordinary Time
My sheep hear my voice, says the Lord; I know them, and they fol - low me.

17 Ordinary Time
A great prophet has risen in our midst. God has visit - ed his peo - ple.

18 Ordinary Time
One does not live on bread a - lone, but on every word that comes forth from the mouth of God.

19 Ordinary Time
I am the living bread that came down from heaven, says the Lord; whoever eats this bread will live for - ev - er.

20 Ordinary Time
Who- ev - er eats my flesh and drinks my blood remains in me and I in him, says the Lord.

21 Ordinary Time
Your words, Lord, are Spirit and life; you have the words of ev - er - last - ing life.

22 Ordinary Time
The Fa - ther willed to give us birth by the word of truth that we may be a kind of firstfruits of his crea - tures.

23 Ordinary Time
Je - sus proclaimed the Gospel of the king - dom and cured every disease a - mong the peo - ple.

24 Ordinary Time
May I never boast except in the cross of our Lord through which the world has been crucified to me and I to the world.

25 Ordinary Time
God has called us through the Gos - pel to possess the glory of our Lord Je - sus Christ.

26 Ordinary Time
Your word, O Lord, is truth; conse - crate us in the truth.

27 Ordinary Time
If we love one another, God re - mains in us and his love is brought to per - fec - tion in us.

28 Ordinary Time
Bless - ed are the poor in spir - it, for theirs is the king - dom of heav - en.

29 Ordinary Time
The Son of Man came to serve and to give his life as a ran - som for man - y.

30 Ordinary Time
Our Sav - ior Jesus Christ de - stroyed death and brought life to light through the Gos - pel.

31 Ordinary Time
Who- ev - er loves me will keep my word, says the Lord; and my Father will love him and we will come to him.

B161b Gospel Acclamation
Revised

RESPONSE

Al - le - lu - ia,___ al - le - lu - ia, al - le - lu - ia.

Music © 1958, 1964, WLP

Robert F. Twynham

VERSES

Cantor/Choir

32 Ordinary Time
Bless - ed   are the poor in   spir - it,   for theirs is the king - dom of heav - en.

33 Ordinary Time
Be vig - ilant at   all   times   and pray that you have
the strength to stand be - fore the Son of Man.

Christ the King
Bless - ed   is he who comes in the name   of the Lord! Blessed is the kingdom
of our father Dav - id   that is   to come!

Nativity of St. John the Baptist, Vigil
He came   to testify   to the light,   to prepare a people   fit for the   Lord.

Nativity of St. John the Baptist, during the Day
You, child,   will be called prophet of the   Most   High,   for you will go before the Lord   to   pre - pare his way.

Music © 2000, WLP

Tone 8G

SS. Peter and Paul, Vigil
Lord, you know ev - 'ry - thing; you know that I love you.

SS. Peter and Paul, during the Day
You are Peter and upon this rock I will build my church, and the gates of the netherworld shall not pre- vail a - gainst it.

Transfiguration
This is my beloved Son with whom I am well pleased; —— lis - ten to him.

Assumption of the Blessed Virgin Mary, Vigil
Bless - ed are they who hear the word of God —— and ob - serve it.

Assumption of the Blessed Virgin Mary, during the Day
Ma - ry is taken up to heav - en; a chorus of an - gels ex - ults.

Exaltation of the Holy Cross
We a - dore you, O Christ, and we bless you, because by your Cross you have re- deemed the world.

All Saints
Come to me, all you who labor and are bur - dened, and I will give you rest, says the Lord.

All Souls
I am the living bread that came down from heaven, says the Lord; whoever eats this bread will live for - ev - er.

Dedication of the Lateran Basilica
I have chosen and consecrated this house, says the Lord, that my name may be there for - ev - er.

Thanksgiving Day
In all circumstances give thanks; for this is the will of God for you in Christ Je - sus.

B162a Gospel Acclamation
Revised
RESPONSE

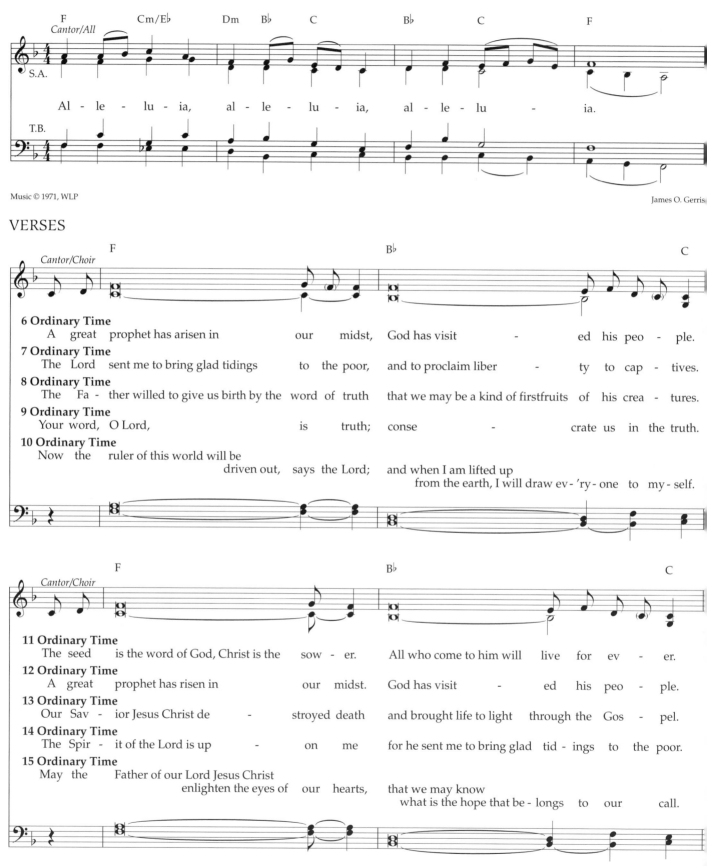

Music © 1971, WLP

James O. Gerris

VERSES

6 Ordinary Time
A great prophet has arisen in our midst, God has visit - ed his peo - ple.

7 Ordinary Time
The Lord sent me to bring glad tidings to the poor, and to proclaim liber - ty to cap - tives.

8 Ordinary Time
The Fa - ther willed to give us birth by the word of truth that we may be a kind of firstfruits of his crea - tures.

9 Ordinary Time
Your word, O Lord, is truth; conse - crate us in the truth.

10 Ordinary Time
Now the ruler of this world will be driven out, says the Lord; and when I am lifted up from the earth, I will draw ev - 'ry- one to my - self.

11 Ordinary Time
The seed is the word of God, Christ is the sow - er. All who come to him will live for ev - er.

12 Ordinary Time
A great prophet has risen in our midst. God has visit - ed his peo - ple.

13 Ordinary Time
Our Sav - ior Jesus Christ de - stroyed death and brought life to light through the Gos - pel.

14 Ordinary Time
The Spir - it of the Lord is up - on me for he sent me to bring glad tid - ings to the poor.

15 Ordinary Time
May the Father of our Lord Jesus Christ enlighten the eyes of our hearts, that we may know what is the hope that be - longs to our call.

Music © 2000, WLP

Tone 8G

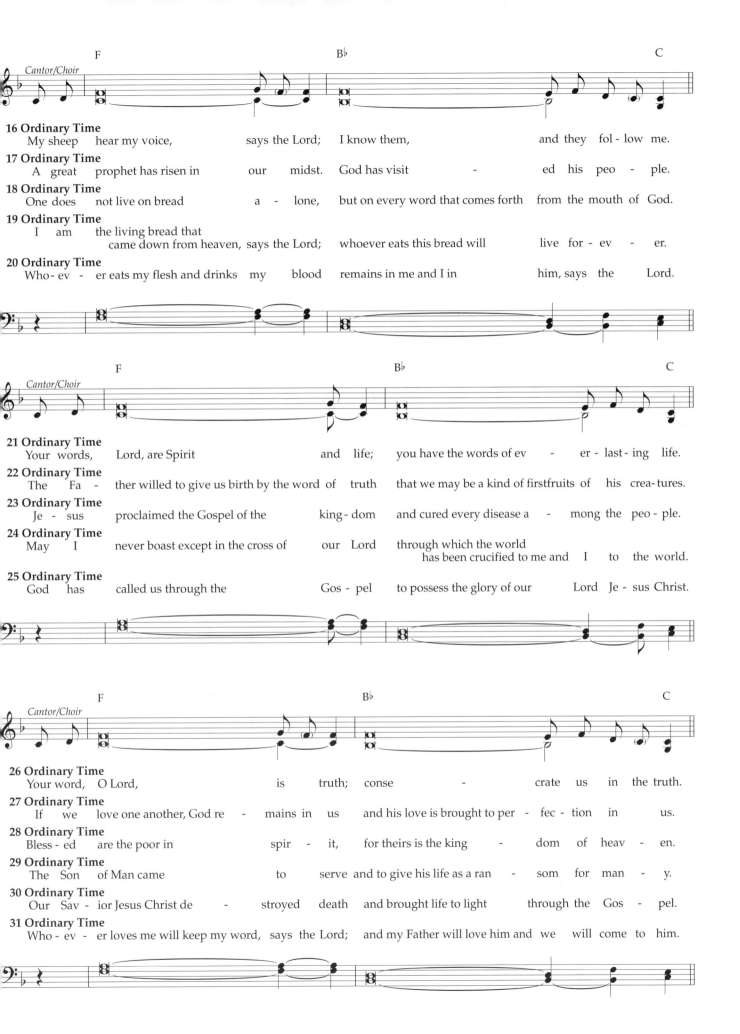

16 Ordinary Time
My sheep hear my voice, says the Lord; I know them, and they fol-low me.

17 Ordinary Time
A great prophet has risen in our midst. God has visit - ed his peo - ple.

18 Ordinary Time
One does not live on bread a - lone, but on every word that comes forth from the mouth of God.

19 Ordinary Time
I am the living bread that came down from heaven, says the Lord; whoever eats this bread will live for - ev - er.

20 Ordinary Time
Who-ev - er eats my flesh and drinks my blood remains in me and I in him, says the Lord.

21 Ordinary Time
Your words, Lord, are Spirit and life; you have the words of ev - er - last - ing life.

22 Ordinary Time
The Fa - ther willed to give us birth by the word of truth that we may be a kind of firstfruits of his crea-tures.

23 Ordinary Time
Je - sus proclaimed the Gospel of the king - dom and cured every disease a - mong the peo - ple.

24 Ordinary Time
May I never boast except in the cross of our Lord through which the world has been crucified to me and I to the world.

25 Ordinary Time
God has called us through the Gos - pel to possess the glory of our Lord Je - sus Christ.

26 Ordinary Time
Your word, O Lord, is truth; conse - crate us in the truth.

27 Ordinary Time
If we love one another, God re - mains in us and his love is brought to per - fec - tion in us.

28 Ordinary Time
Bless - ed are the poor in spir - it, for theirs is the king - dom of heav - en.

29 Ordinary Time
The Son of Man came to serve and to give his life as a ran - som for man - y.

30 Ordinary Time
Our Sav - ior Jesus Christ de - stroyed death and brought life to light through the Gos - pel.

31 Ordinary Time
Who-ev - er loves me will keep my word, says the Lord; and my Father will love him and we will come to him.

B162b Gospel Acclamation
Revised

RESPONSE

Al - le - lu - ia, al - le - lu - ia, al - le - lu - ia.

James O. Gerris

VERSES

32 Ordinary Time
Bless - ed are the poor in spir - it, for theirs is the king - dom of heav - en.

33 Ordinary Time
Be vig - ilant at all times and pray that you have the strength to stand be - fore the Son of Man.

Christ the King
Bless - ed is he who comes in the name of the Lord! Blessed is the kingdom of our father Dav - id that is to come!

Nativity of St. John the Baptist, Vigil
He came to testify to the light, to prepare a people fit for the Lord.

Nativity of St. John the Baptist, during the Day
You, child, will be called prophet of the Most High, for you will go before the Lord to pre - pare his way.

Tone 8C

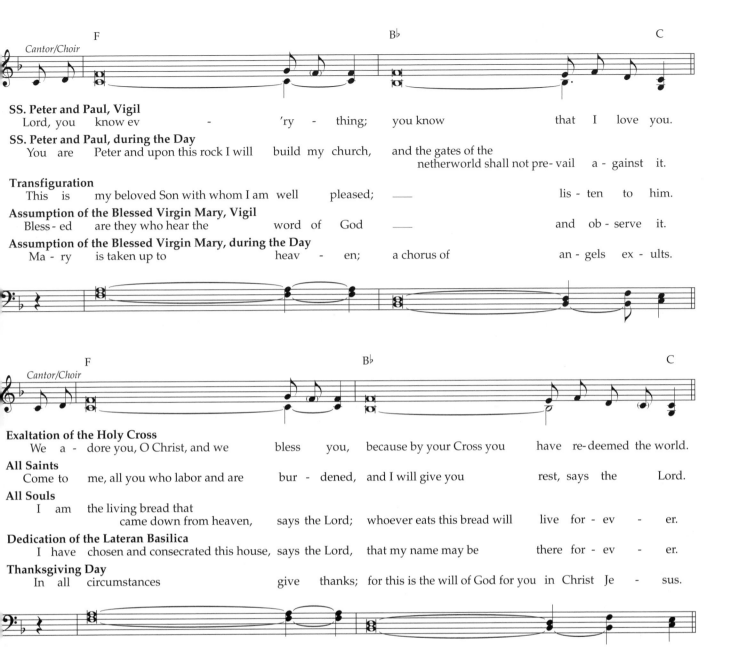

SS. Peter and Paul, Vigil
Lord, you know ev - 'ry - thing; you know that I love you.

SS. Peter and Paul, during the Day
You are Peter and upon this rock I will build my church, and the gates of the netherworld shall not pre- vail a - gainst it.

Transfiguration
This is my beloved Son with whom I am well pleased; —— lis - ten to him.

Assumption of the Blessed Virgin Mary, Vigil
Bless - ed are they who hear the word of God —— and ob - serve it.

Assumption of the Blessed Virgin Mary, during the Day
Ma - ry is taken up to heav - en; a chorus of an - gels ex - ults.

Exaltation of the Holy Cross
We a - dore you, O Christ, and we bless you, because by your Cross you have re-deemed the world.

All Saints
Come to me, all you who labor and are bur - dened, and I will give you rest, says the Lord.

All Souls
I am the living bread that came down from heaven, says the Lord; whoever eats this bread will live for - ev - er.

Dedication of the Lateran Basilica
I have chosen and consecrated this house, says the Lord, that my name may be there for - ev - er.

Thanksgiving Day
In all circumstances give thanks; for this is the will of God for you in Christ Je - sus.

B163a Gospel Acclamation
Revised

RESPONSE

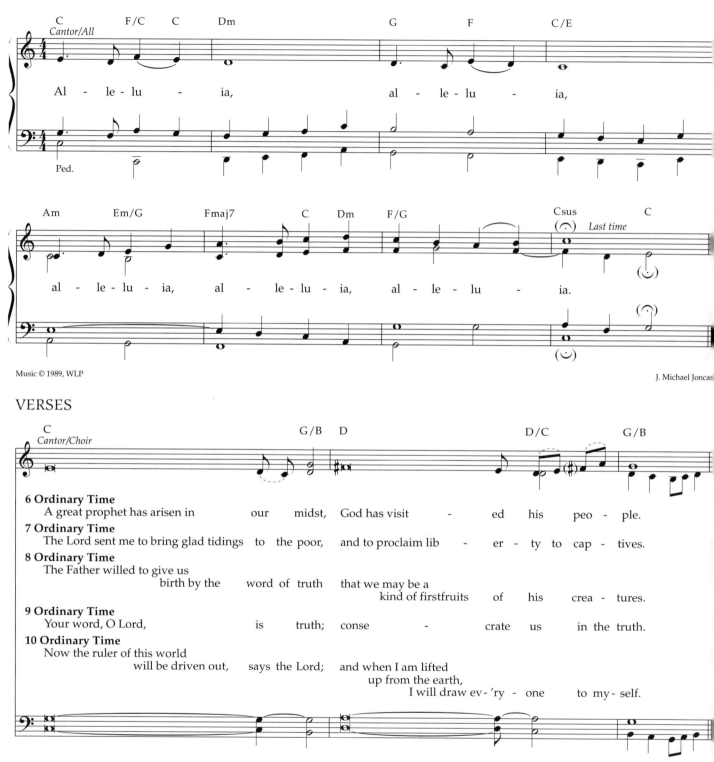

Al - le - lu - ia, al - le - lu - ia,

al - le - lu - ia, al - le - lu - ia, al - le - lu - ia.

Last time

Music © 1989, WLP

J. Michael Joncas

VERSES

Cantor/Choir

6 Ordinary Time
A great prophet has arisen in our midst, God has visit - ed his peo - ple.

7 Ordinary Time
The Lord sent me to bring glad tidings to the poor, and to proclaim lib - er - ty to cap - tives.

8 Ordinary Time
The Father willed to give us birth by the word of truth that we may be a kind of firstfruits of his crea - tures.

9 Ordinary Time
Your word, O Lord, is truth; conse - crate us in the truth.

10 Ordinary Time
Now the ruler of this world will be driven out, says the Lord; and when I am lifted up from the earth, I will draw ev - 'ry - one to my - self.

Music © 1989, WLP

J. Michael Joncas

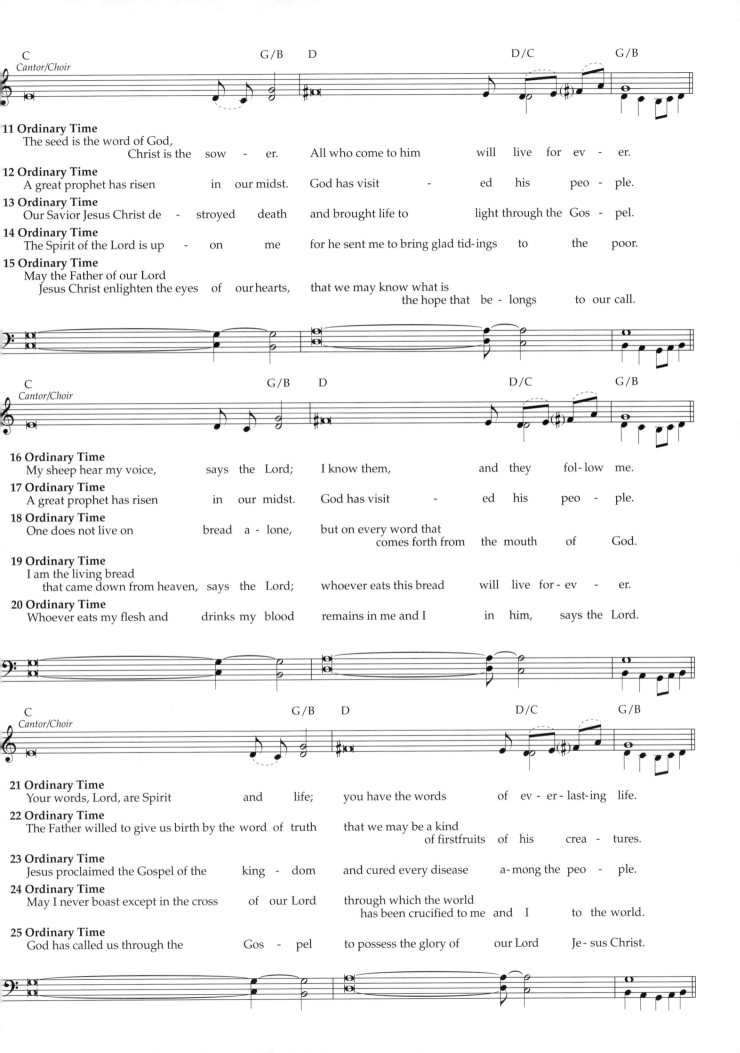

11 Ordinary Time
The seed is the word of God,
Christ is the sow - er. All who come to him will live for ev - er.

12 Ordinary Time
A great prophet has risen in our midst. God has visit - ed his peo - ple.

13 Ordinary Time
Our Savior Jesus Christ de - stroyed death and brought life to light through the Gos - pel.

14 Ordinary Time
The Spirit of the Lord is up - on me for he sent me to bring glad tid-ings to the poor.

15 Ordinary Time
May the Father of our Lord
Jesus Christ enlighten the eyes of our hearts, that we may know what is
the hope that be - longs to our call.

16 Ordinary Time
My sheep hear my voice, says the Lord; I know them, and they fol-low me.

17 Ordinary Time
A great prophet has risen in our midst. God has visit - ed his peo - ple.

18 Ordinary Time
One does not live on bread a - lone, but on every word that
comes forth from the mouth of God.

19 Ordinary Time
I am the living bread
that came down from heaven, says the Lord; whoever eats this bread will live for - ev - er.

20 Ordinary Time
Whoever eats my flesh and drinks my blood remains in me and I in him, says the Lord.

21 Ordinary Time
Your words, Lord, are Spirit and life; you have the words of ev - er - last-ing life.

22 Ordinary Time
The Father willed to give us birth by the word of truth that we may be a kind
of firstfruits of his crea - tures.

23 Ordinary Time
Jesus proclaimed the Gospel of the king - dom and cured every disease a-mong the peo - ple.

24 Ordinary Time
May I never boast except in the cross of our Lord through which the world
has been crucified to me and I to the world.

25 Ordinary Time
God has called us through the Gos - pel to possess the glory of our Lord Je - sus Christ.

B163b Gospel Acclamation
Revised

RESPONSE

Al - le - lu - ia,   al - le - lu - ia,

al - le - lu - ia,   al - le - lu - ia,   al - le - lu - ia.

Music © 1989, WLP

J. Michael Jonca

VERSES

26 Ordinary Time
Your word, O Lord, is truth; conse - crate us in the truth.

27 Ordinary Time
If we love one another, God re - mains in us and his love is brought to per - fec - tion in us.

28 Ordinary Time
Blessed are the poor in spir - it, for theirs is the king - dom of heav - en.

29 Ordinary Time
The Son of Man came to serve and to give his life as a ran - som for man - y.

30 Ordinary Time
Our Savior Jesus Christ de - stroyed death and brought life to light through the Gos - pel.

31 Ordinary Time
Whoever loves me will keep my word, says the Lord; and my Father will love him and we will come to him.

Music © 1989, WLP

J. Michael Jonca

32 Ordinary Time
Blessed are the poor in spir - it, for theirs is the king - dom of heav - en.

33 Ordinary Time
Be vigilant at all times and pray that you have the strength to stand be-fore the Son of Man.

Christ the King
Blessed is he who comes in the name of the Lord! Blessed is the kingdom of our father David that is to come!

Nativity of St. John the Baptist, Vigil
He came to testify to the light, to prepare a peo - ple fit for the Lord.

Nativity of St. John the Baptist, during the Day
You, child, will be called prophet of the Most High, for you will go before the Lord to pre pare his way.

SS. Peter and Paul, Vigil
Lord, you know ev - 'ry - thing; you know that I love you.

SS. Peter and Paul, during the Day
You are Peter and upon this rock I will build my church, and the gates of the netherworld shall not pre-vail a-gainst it.

Transfiguration
This is my beloved Son with whom I am well pleased; ⎯ ⎯ lis - ten to him.

Assumption of the Blessed Virgin Mary, Vigil
Blessed are they who hear the word of God ⎯ ⎯ and ob-serve it.

Assumption of the Blessed Virgin Mary, during the Day
Mary is taken up to heaven; a chorus of an - gels ex-ults.

B163c   Gospel Acclamation
Revised

RESPONSE

Al - le - lu - ia, al - le - lu - ia,

al - le - lu - ia, al - le - lu - ia, al - le - lu - ia.

J. Michael Joncas

VERSES

Cantor/Choir

Exaltation of the Holy Cross
We adore you, O Christ,   and we bless you, because by your Cross you have re-deemed   the   world.

All Saints
Come to me, all you who labor and are burdened, and I will give   you   rest,   says the Lord.

All Souls
I am the living bread
   that came down from heaven, says the   Lord;   whoever eats this bread   will   live for - ev - er.

Dedication of the Lateran Basilica
I have chosen and
      consecrated this house, says the   Lord,   that my name may   be   there for - ev - er.

Thanksgiving Day
In all circumstances   give   thanks;   for this is the will of God for you in   Christ   Je - sus.

J. Michael Joncas

RESPONSE

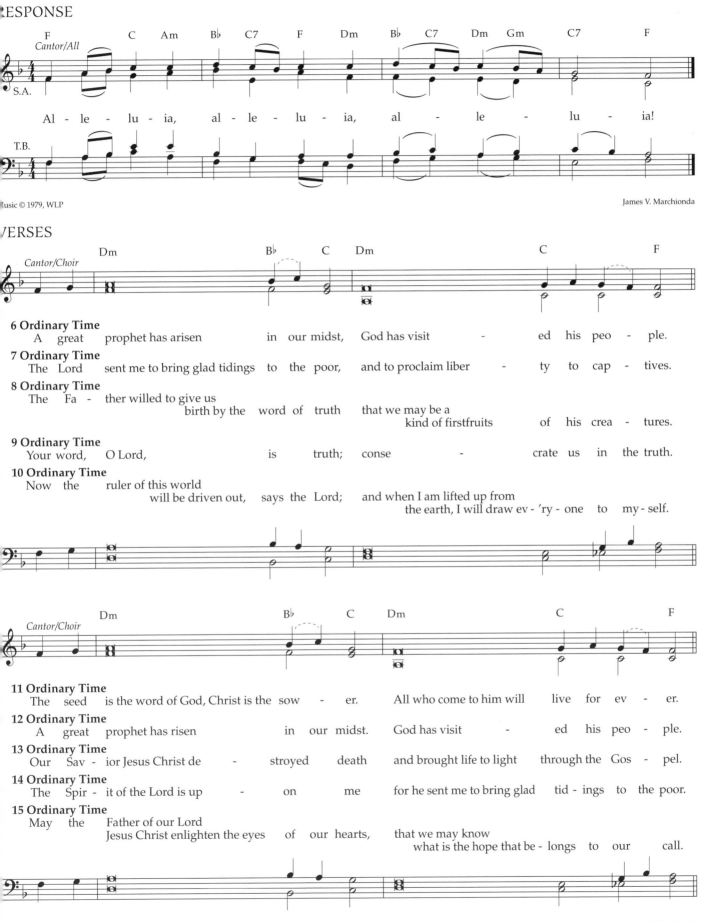

Cantor/All

S.A.

Al - le - lu - ia, al - le - lu - ia, al - le - lu - ia!

T.B.

Music © 1979, WLP

James V. Marchionda

VERSES

Cantor/Choir

6 Ordinary Time
A great prophet has arisen in our midst, God has visit - ed his peo - ple.

7 Ordinary Time
The Lord sent me to bring glad tidings to the poor, and to proclaim liber - ty to cap - tives.

8 Ordinary Time
The Fa - ther willed to give us birth by the word of truth that we may be a kind of firstfruits of his crea - tures.

9 Ordinary Time
Your word, O Lord, is truth; conse - crate us in the truth.

10 Ordinary Time
Now the ruler of this world will be driven out, says the Lord; and when I am lifted up from the earth, I will draw ev - 'ry - one to my - self.

Cantor/Choir

11 Ordinary Time
The seed is the word of God, Christ is the sow - er. All who come to him will live for ev - er.

12 Ordinary Time
A great prophet has risen in our midst. God has visit - ed his peo - ple.

13 Ordinary Time
Our Sav - ior Jesus Christ de - stroyed death and brought life to light through the Gos - pel.

14 Ordinary Time
The Spir - it of the Lord is up - on me for he sent me to bring glad tid - ings to the poor.

15 Ordinary Time
May the Father of our Lord Jesus Christ enlighten the eyes of our hearts, that we may know what is the hope that be - longs to our call.

Music © 1984, WLP

James V. Marchionda

B164b Gospel Acclamation
Revised

RESPONSE

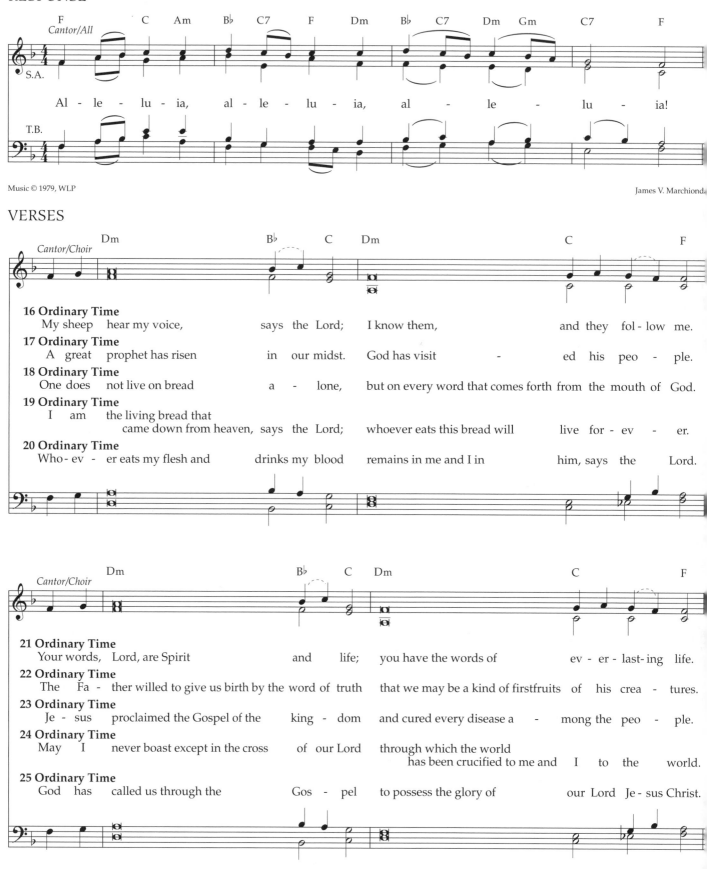

Al - le - lu - ia, al - le - lu - ia, al - le - lu - ia!

Music © 1979, WLP

James V. Marchionda

VERSES

16 Ordinary Time
My sheep hear my voice, says the Lord; I know them, and they fol - low me.

17 Ordinary Time
A great prophet has risen in our midst. God has visit - ed his peo - ple.

18 Ordinary Time
One does not live on bread a - lone, but on every word that comes forth from the mouth of God.

19 Ordinary Time
I am the living bread that came down from heaven, says the Lord; whoever eats this bread will live for - ev - er.

20 Ordinary Time
Who - ev - er eats my flesh and drinks my blood remains in me and I in him, says the Lord.

21 Ordinary Time
Your words, Lord, are Spirit and life; you have the words of ev - er - last - ing life.

22 Ordinary Time
The Fa - ther willed to give us birth by the word of truth that we may be a kind of firstfruits of his crea - tures.

23 Ordinary Time
Je - sus proclaimed the Gospel of the king - dom and cured every disease a - mong the peo - ple.

24 Ordinary Time
May I never boast except in the cross of our Lord through which the world has been crucified to me and I to the world.

25 Ordinary Time
God has called us through the Gos - pel to possess the glory of our Lord Je - sus Christ.

Music © 1984, WLP

James V. Marchionda

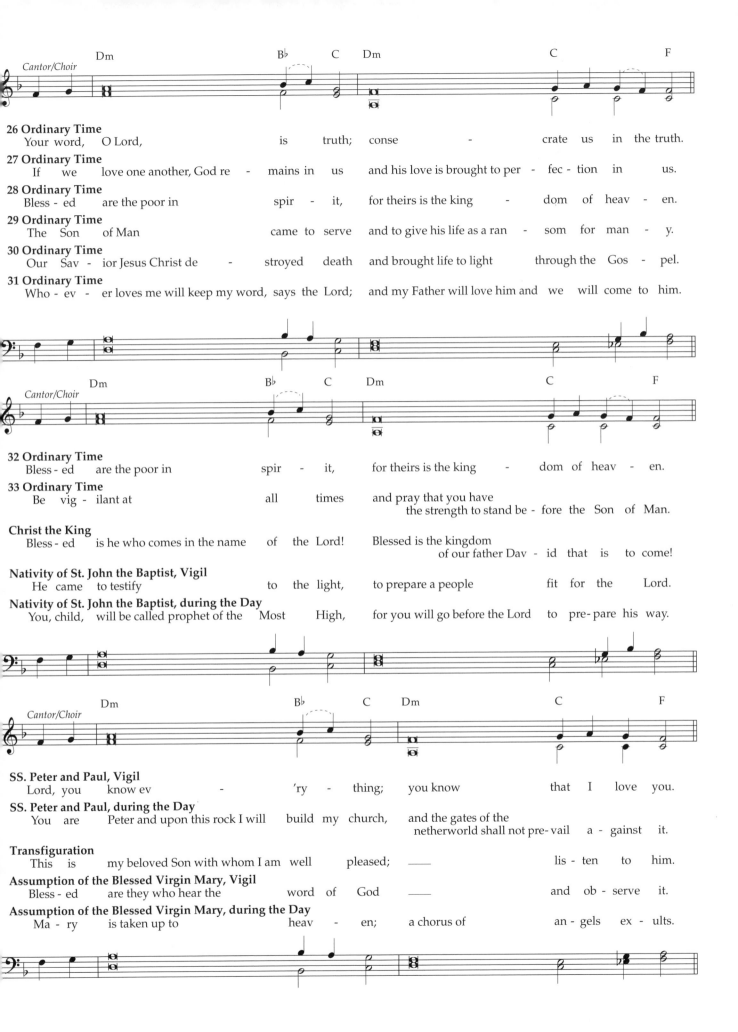

26 Ordinary Time
Your word, O Lord, is truth; conse - crate us in the truth.

27 Ordinary Time
If we love one another, God re - mains in us and his love is brought to per - fec - tion in us.

28 Ordinary Time
Bless - ed are the poor in spir - it, for theirs is the king - dom of heav - en.

29 Ordinary Time
The Son of Man came to serve and to give his life as a ran - som for man - y.

30 Ordinary Time
Our Sav - ior Jesus Christ de - stroyed death and brought life to light through the Gos - pel.

31 Ordinary Time
Who - ev - er loves me will keep my word, says the Lord; and my Father will love him and we will come to him.

32 Ordinary Time
Bless - ed are the poor in spir - it, for theirs is the king - dom of heav - en.

33 Ordinary Time
Be vig - ilant at all times and pray that you have the strength to stand be - fore the Son of Man.

Christ the King
Bless - ed is he who comes in the name of the Lord! Blessed is the kingdom of our father Dav - id that is to come!

Nativity of St. John the Baptist, Vigil
He came to testify to the light, to prepare a people fit for the Lord.

Nativity of St. John the Baptist, during the Day
You, child, will be called prophet of the Most High, for you will go before the Lord to pre - pare his way.

SS. Peter and Paul, Vigil
Lord, you know ev - 'ry - thing; you know that I love you.

SS. Peter and Paul, during the Day
You are Peter and upon this rock I will build my church, and the gates of the netherworld shall not pre - vail a - gainst it.

Transfiguration
This is my beloved Son with whom I am well pleased; ___ lis - ten to him.

Assumption of the Blessed Virgin Mary, Vigil
Bless - ed are they who hear the word of God ___ and ob - serve it.

Assumption of the Blessed Virgin Mary, during the Day
Ma - ry is taken up to heav - en; a chorus of an - gels ex - ults.

B164c Gospel Acclamation
Revised

RESPONSE

Cantor/All

Al - le - lu - ia, al - le - lu - ia, al - le - lu - ia!

Music © 1979, WLP

James V. Marchionda

VERSES

Cantor/Choir

Exaltation of the Holy Cross
We a - dore you, O Christ, and we bless you, because by your Cross you have re-deemed the world.

All Saints
Come to me, all you who labor and are bur - dened, and I will give you rest, says the Lord.

All Souls
I am the living bread that came down from heaven, says the Lord; whoever eats this bread will live for - ev - er.

Dedication of the Lateran Basilica
I have chosen and consecrated this house, says the Lord, that my name may be there for - ev - er.

Thanksgiving Day
In all circumstances give thanks; for this is the will of God for you in Christ Je - sus.

Music © 1984, WLP

James V. Marchionda

RESPONSE

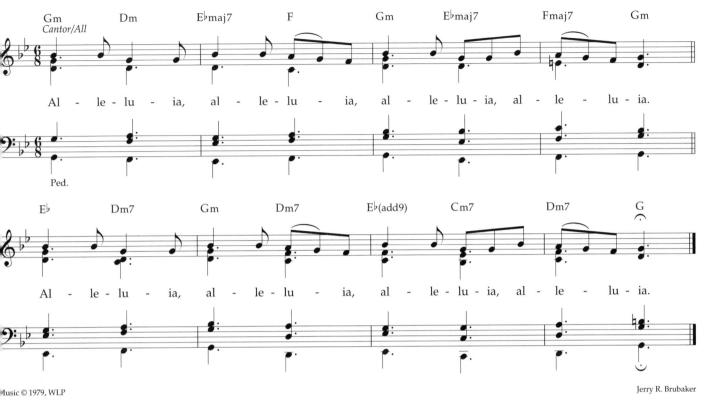

Al - le - lu - ia, al - le - lu - ia, al - le - lu - ia, al - le - lu - ia.

Al - le - lu - ia, al - le - lu - ia, al - le - lu - ia, al - le - lu - ia.

Music © 1979, WLP

Jerry R. Brubaker

Choral harmony and descant may be found at B175.

VERSES

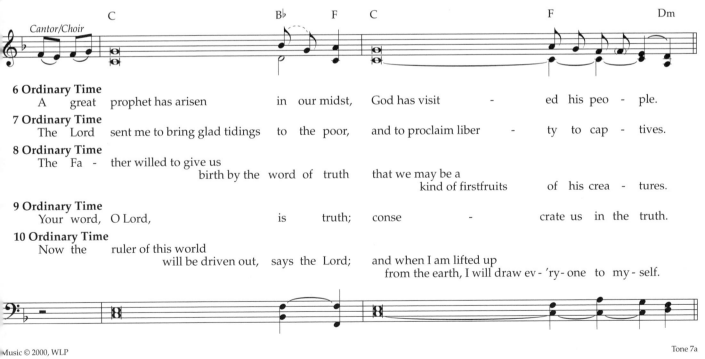

6 Ordinary Time
A great prophet has arisen in our midst, God has visit - ed his peo - ple.

7 Ordinary Time
The Lord sent me to bring glad tidings to the poor, and to proclaim liber - ty to cap - tives.

8 Ordinary Time
The Fa - ther willed to give us birth by the word of truth that we may be a kind of firstfruits of his crea - tures.

9 Ordinary Time
Your word, O Lord, is truth; conse - crate us in the truth.

10 Ordinary Time
Now the ruler of this world will be driven out, says the Lord; and when I am lifted up from the earth, I will draw ev - 'ry - one to my - self.

Music © 2000, WLP

Tone 7a

B165b Gospel Acclamation

Revised

RESPONSE

Al - le - lu - ia, al - le - lu - ia, al - le - lu - ia, al - le - lu - ia.

Al - le - lu - ia, al - le - lu - ia, al - le - lu - ia, al - le - lu - ia.

Jerry R. Brubaker

Choral harmony and descant may be found at B175.

VERSES

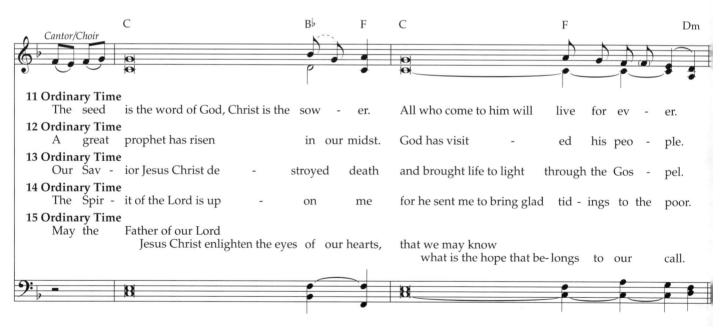

11 Ordinary Time
The seed is the word of God, Christ is the sow - er. All who come to him will live for ev - er.

12 Ordinary Time
A great prophet has risen in our midst. God has visit - ed his peo - ple.

13 Ordinary Time
Our Sav - ior Jesus Christ de - stroyed death and brought life to light through the Gos - pel.

14 Ordinary Time
The Spir - it of the Lord is up - on me for he sent me to bring glad tid - ings to the poor.

15 Ordinary Time
May the Father of our Lord
Jesus Christ enlighten the eyes of our hearts, that we may know
what is the hope that be - longs to our call.

Tone 7a

16 Ordinary Time
My sheep hear my voice, says the Lord; I know them, and they fol - low me.

17 Ordinary Time
A great prophet has risen in our midst. God has visit - ed his peo - ple.

18 Ordinary Time
One does not live on bread a - lone, but on every word that comes forth from the mouth of God.

19 Ordinary Time
I am the living bread that came down from heaven, says the Lord; whoever eats this bread will live for - ev - er.

20 Ordinary Time
Who-ev - er eats my flesh and drinks my blood remains in me and I in him, says the Lord.

21 Ordinary Time
Your words, Lord, are Spirit and life; you have the words of ev - er - last-ing life.

22 Ordinary Time
The Fa - ther willed to give us birth by the word of truth that we may be a kind of firstfruits of his crea - tures.

23 Ordinary Time
Je - sus proclaimed the Gospel of the king - dom and cured every disease a - mong the peo - ple.

24 Ordinary Time
May I never boast except in the cross of our Lord through which the world has been crucified to me and I to the world.

25 Ordinary Time
God has called us through the Gos - pel to possess the glory of our Lord Je - sus Christ.

26 Ordinary Time
Your word, O Lord, is truth; conse - crate us in the truth.

27 Ordinary Time
If we love one another, God re - mains in us and his love is brought to per - fec - tion in us.

28 Ordinary Time
Bless - ed are the poor in spir - it, for theirs is the king - dom of heav - en.

29 Ordinary Time
The Son of Man came to serve and to give his life as a ran - som for man - y.

30 Ordinary Time
Our Sav - ior Jesus Christ de - stroyed death and brought life to light through the Gos - pel.

31 Ordinary Time
Who-ev - er loves me will keep my word, says the Lord; and my Father will love him and we will come to him.

Tone 7a

B165c Gospel Acclamation
Revised

RESPONSE

Al - le - lu - ia, al - le - lu - ia, al - le - lu - ia, al - le - lu - ia.

Al - le - lu - ia, al - le - lu - ia, al - le - lu - ia, al - le - lu - ia.

Music © 1979, WLP   Jerry R. Brubaker

Choral harmony and descant may be found at B175.

VERSES

32 Ordinary Time
Bless-ed   are the poor in   spir - it,   for theirs is the king - dom of heav - en.

33 Ordinary Time
Be   vig - ilant at   all   times   and pray that you have
the strength to stand be - fore the Son of Man.

Christ the King
Bless-ed   is he who comes in the name   of   the Lord! Blessed is the kingdom
of our father Dav - id   that   is   to   come!

Nativity of St. John the Baptist, Vigil
He   came to testify   to   the light,   to prepare a people   fit   for the   Lord.

Nativity of St. John the Baptist, during the Day
You, child, will be called prophet of the   Most   High, for you will go before the Lord   to   pre-pare his   way.

Music © 2000, WLP   Tone 7a

SS. Peter and Paul, Vigil
Lord, you know ev - 'ry - thing; you know that I love you.

SS. Peter and Paul, during the Day
You are Peter and upon this rock I will build my church, and the gates of the netherworld shall not pre- vail a- gainst it.

Transfiguration
This is my beloved Son with whom I am well pleased; ____ lis - ten to him.

Assumption of the Blessed Virgin Mary, Vigil
Bless- ed are they who hear the word of God ____ and ob- serve it.

Assumption of the Blessed Virgin Mary, during the Day
Ma - ry is taken up to heav - en; a chorus of an - gels ex - ults.

Exaltation of the Holy Cross
We a - dore you, O Christ, and we bless you, because by your Cross you have re-deemed the world.

All Saints
Come to me, all you who labor and are bur - dened, and I will give you rest, says the Lord.

All Souls
I am the living bread that came down from heaven, says the Lord; whoever eats this bread will live for - ev - er.

Dedication of the Lateran Basilica
I have chosen and consecrated this house, says the Lord, that my name may be there for - ev - er.

Thanksgiving Day
In all circumstances give thanks; for this is the will of God for you in Christ Je - sus.

Tone 7a

B166 Gospel Acclamation—Funeral
Revised

RESPONSE

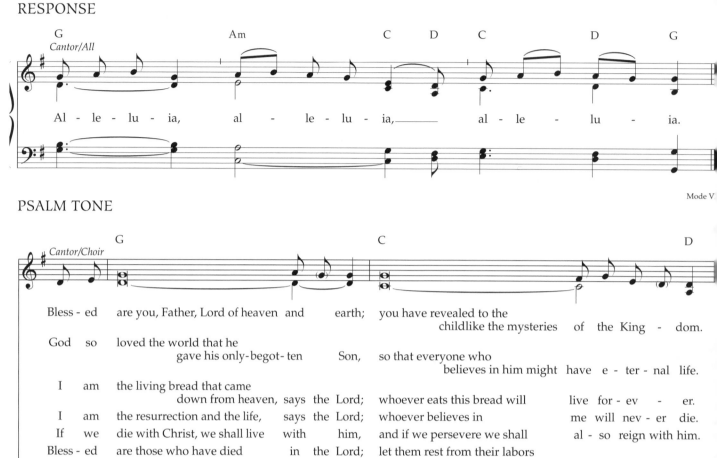

Al - le - lu - ia, al - le - lu - ia,_____ al - le - lu - ia.

Mode V

PSALM TONE

Music © 2000, WLP

Tone 8C

Bless - ed are you, Father, Lord of heaven and earth; you have revealed to the childlike the mysteries of the King - dom.

God so loved the world that he gave his only-begot- ten Son, so that everyone who believes in him might have e - ter - nal life.

I am the living bread that came down from heaven, says the Lord; whoever eats this bread will live for - ev - er.

I am the resurrection and the life, says the Lord; whoever believes in me will nev - er die.

If we die with Christ, we shall live with him, and if we persevere we shall al - so reign with him.

Bless - ed are those who have died in the Lord; let them rest from their labors for their good deeds go with them.

RESPONSE

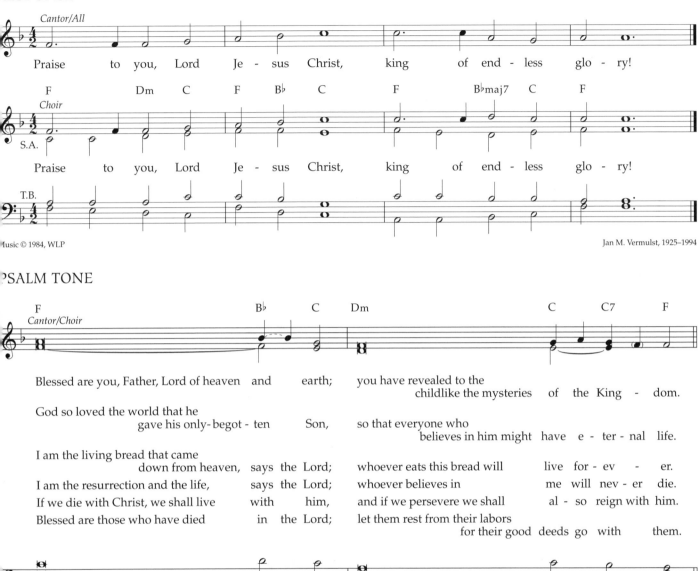

Cantor/All

Praise to you, Lord Je - sus Christ, king of end - less glo - ry!

F   Dm   C   F   B♭   C   F   B♭maj7   C   F

Choir

S.A.

Praise to you, Lord Je - sus Christ, king of end - less glo - ry!

T.B.

Jan M. Vermulst, 1925–1994

PSALM TONE

F   B♭   C   Dm   C   C7   F

Cantor/Choir

Blessed are you, Father, Lord of heaven and earth; you have revealed to the
childlike the mysteries of the King - dom.

God so loved the world that he
gave his only-begot - ten Son, so that everyone who
believes in him might have e - ter - nal life.

I am the living bread that came
down from heaven, says the Lord; whoever eats this bread will live for - ev - er.

I am the resurrection and the life, says the Lord; whoever believes in me will nev - er die.

If we die with Christ, we shall live with him, and if we persevere we shall al - so reign with him.

Blessed are those who have died in the Lord; let them rest from their labors
for their good deeds go with them.

Jan M. Vermulst, 1925–1994

B168 Gospel Acclamation
Revised

RESPONSE

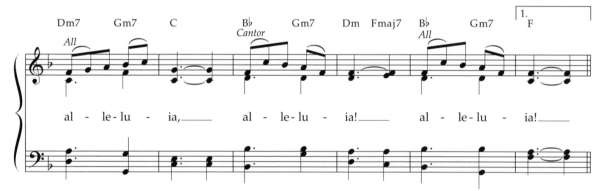

James J. Chepponis

PSALM TONE

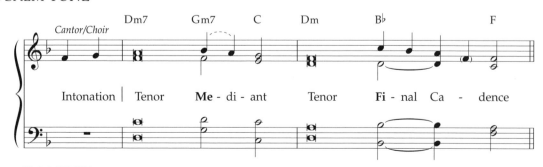

James J. Chepponis

RESPONSE

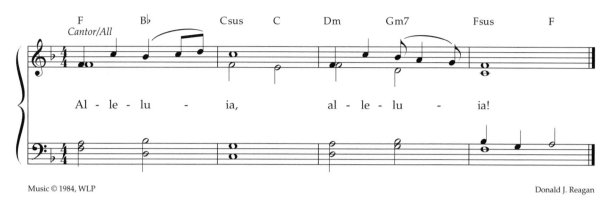

Al - le - lu - ia, al - le - lu - ia!

Donald J. Reagan

PSALM TONE

Intonation | Tenor **Me** - di - ant Tenor **Fi** - nal Ca - dence

Donald J. Reagan

B170 Gospel Acclamation
Revised

RESPONSE

Al-le-lu - ia, al-le-lu - ia, al-le-lu - ia.

David C. Isele

PSALM TONE

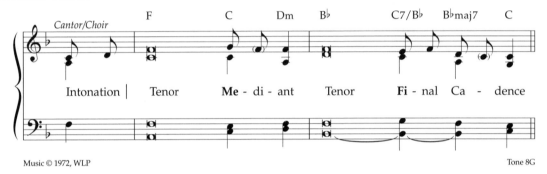

Intonation | Tenor **Me** - di - ant Tenor **Fi** - nal Ca - dence

Tone 8G

Gospel Acclamation B171
Revised

RESPONSE

Al - le - lu - ia,   al - le - lu - ia.

Music © 1970, 1973, WLP

Lucien Deiss

PSALM TONE

Intonation | Tenor   **Me** - di - ant   Tenor   **Fi** - nal Ca - dence

Music © 1972, WLP

Tone 8c

B172 Gospel Acclamation
Revised

RESPONSE

Paul M. French

PSALM TONE

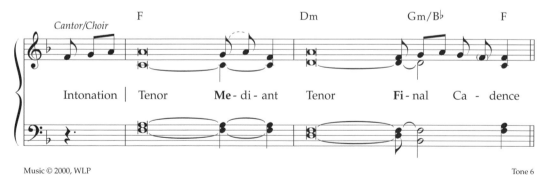

Intonation | Tenor **Me**-di-ant Tenor **Fi**-nal Ca-dence

Tone 6

Gospel Acclamation **B173**
Revised

RESPONSE

Music © 1979, WLP

Howard L. Hughes

PSALM TONE

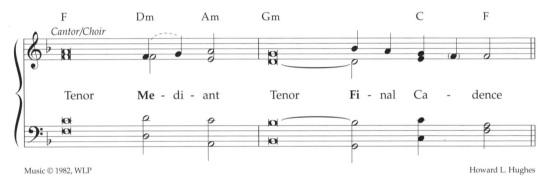

Music © 1982, WLP

Howard L. Hughes

B174 Gospel Acclamation
Revised

RESPONSE

Music © 2000, WLP

Steven R. Janco

PSALM TONE

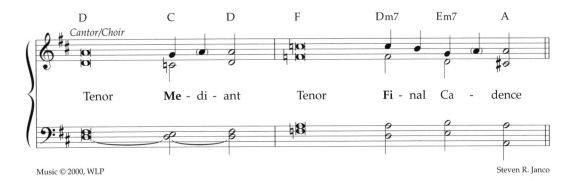

Steven R. Janco

B175 Gospel Acclamation
Revised

RESPONSE

Music © 1979, WLP

Jerry R. Brubaker

PSALM TONE

Music © 1981, WLP

Tone 7a, adapt.

RESPONSE

Eugene E. Englert

PSALM TONE

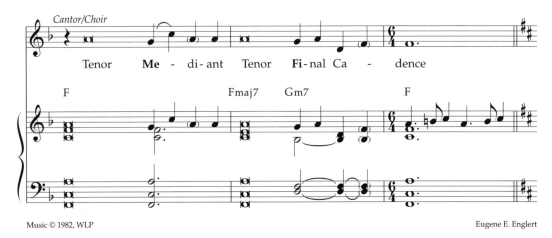

Eugene E. Englert

RESPONSE

Eugene E. Englert

B177 Lenten Gospel Acclamation
Revised

RESPONSE

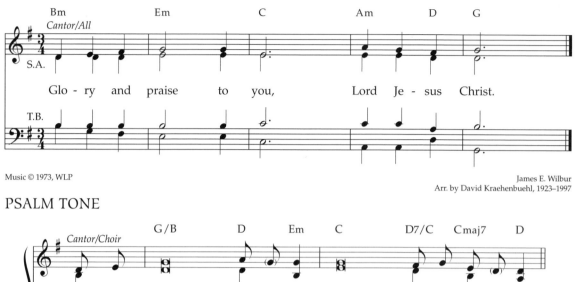

Glo - ry and praise to you, Lord Je - sus Christ.

Music © 1973, WLP

James E. Wilbur
Arr. by David Kraehenbuehl, 1923–1997

PSALM TONE

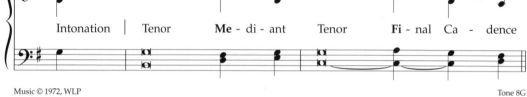

Intonation | Tenor **Me** - di - ant Tenor **Fi** - nal Ca - dence

Music © 1972, WLP

Tone 8G

RESPONSE

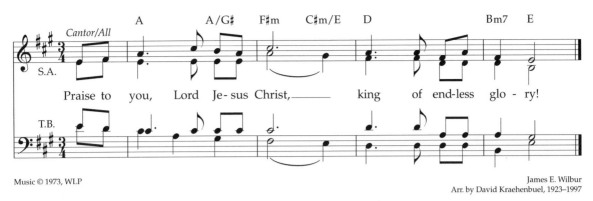

Praise to you, Lord Jesus Christ, king of endless glory!

Music © 1973, WLP

James E. Wilbur
Arr. by David Kraehenbuel, 1923–1997

PSALM TONE

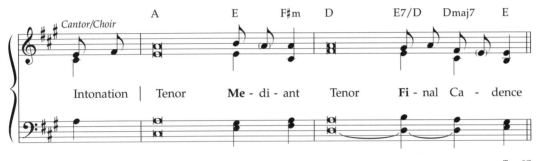

Intonation | Tenor **Me** - di - ant Tenor **Fi** - nal Ca - dence

Music © 1972, WLP

Tone 8G

B179 Lenten Gospel Acclamation
Revised

RESPONSE

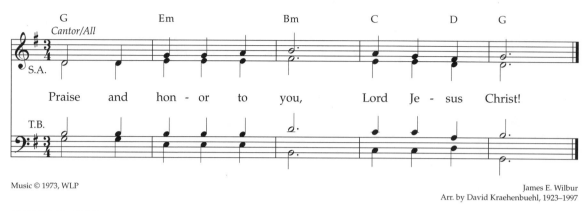

Praise and hon-or to you, Lord Je-sus Christ!

James E. Wilbur
Arr. by David Kraehenbuehl, 1923–1997

PSALM TONE

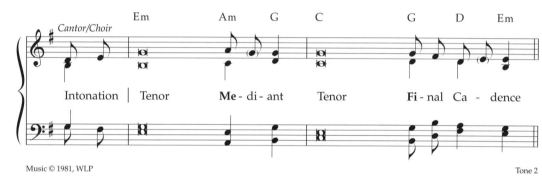

Intonation | Tenor **Me**-di-ant Tenor **Fi**-nal Ca-dence

Tone 2

RESPONSE

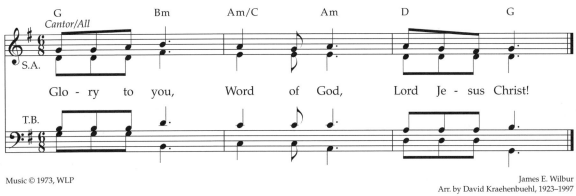

Glo - ry to you, Word of God, Lord Je - sus Christ!

Music © 1973, WLP

James E. Wilbur
Arr. by David Kraehenbuehl, 1923–1997

PSALM TONE

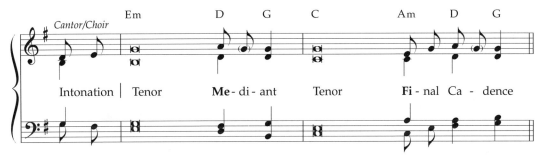

Intonation | Tenor **Me** - di - ant Tenor **Fi** - nal Ca - dence

Music © 1972, WLP

Tone 8c

B181 Lenten Gospel Acclamation
Revised

RESPONSE

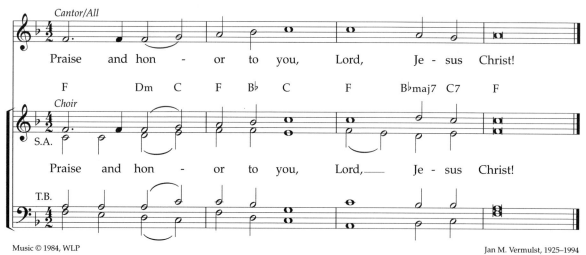

Praise and hon - or to you, Lord, Je - sus Christ!

Praise and hon - or to you, Lord,—— Je - sus Christ!

Jan M. Vermulst, 1925–1994

PSALM TONE

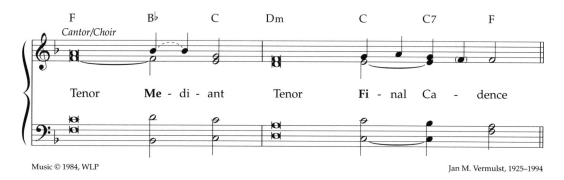

Tenor **Me** - di - ant   Tenor   **Fi** - nal Ca - dence

Jan M. Vermulst, 1925–1994

Lenten Gospel Acclamation B182

Revised

RESPONSE

Glo - ry and praise to you, Lord Je - sus Christ!

Robert J. Schaffer

PSALM TONE

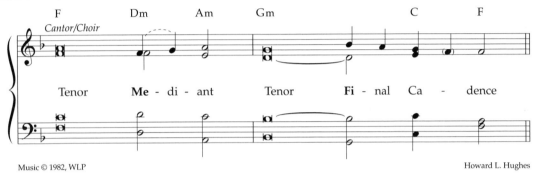

Tenor **Me** - di - ant Tenor **Fi** - nal Ca - dence

Howard L. Hughes

B183 Lenten Gospel Acclamation

Revised

RESPONSE

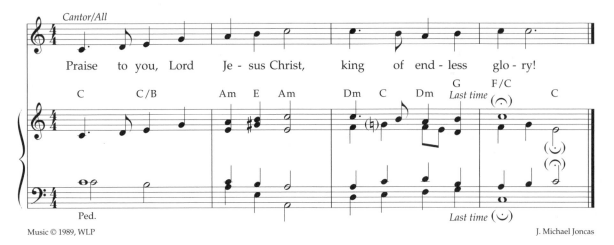

Praise to you, Lord Je-sus Christ, king of end-less glo-ry!

J. Michael Joncas

PSALM TONE

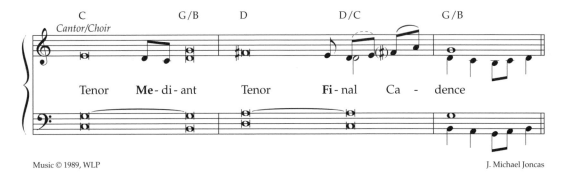

Tenor **Me**-di-ant Tenor **Fi**-nal Ca-dence

J. Michael Joncas

RESPONSE

Glo - ry and praise to you, Lord Je - sus Christ!

Glo - ry and praise to you, Lord Je - sus Christ!

Music © 2000, WLP

Steven R. Janco

PSALM TONE

Tenor Me - di - ant Tenor Fi - nal Ca - dence

Music © 2000, WLP

Steven R. Janco

B185 Lenten Gospel Acclamation
Revised

RESPONSE

Charles Gardner

PSALM TONE

Tenor **Me** - di - ant   Tenor **Fi** - nal Ca - dence

Charles Gardner

Index of Psalms

Index of Other Music

May God bless us in his mercy. — B12
May the Lord bless us all the days of our lives. — B97
My God, my God, why have you abandoned me? — B29, B135
My soul is thirsting for you, O Lord my God. — B143
My soul rejoices in my God. — B3
Our blessing-cup is a communion with the Blood of Christ. — B35
Our eyes are fixed on the Lord, pleading for his mercy. — B84
Out of the depths I cry to you, O Lord. — B128
Praise the Lord, my soul! — B93, B102
Praise the Lord, who heals the brokenhearted. — B75
Since my mother's womb, you have been my strength. — B108
Sing to the Lord a new song, for he has done marvelous deeds. — B118
Sing with joy to God our help. — B79
Taste and see the goodness of the Lord. — B89, B90, B91
Teach me your ways, O Lord. — B73
The angel of the Lord will rescue those who fear him. — B111
The children of Jerusalem...cloaks — B28
The children of Jerusalem...olive branches — B27
The earth is full of the goodness of the Lord. — B42
The hand of the Lord feeds us; he answers all our needs. — B87
The Lord gave them bread from heaven. — B88
The Lord has done great things for us; we are filled with joy. — B100
The Lord has revealed to the nations his saving power. — B62
The Lord has set his throne in heaven. — B64
The Lord is kind and merciful. — B78, B126, B146
The Lord is king; he is robed in majesty. — B104
The Lord is king, the most high over all the earth. — B112
The Lord is my light and my salvation — B31, B125, B141
The Lord is my shepherd; there is nothing I shall want. — B23, B86, B124
The Lord remembers his covenant for ever. — B11
The Lord speaks of peace to his people. — B123
The Lord upholds my life. — B95
The Lord will bless his people with peace. — B15
The one who does justice will live in the presence of the Lord. — B92
The precepts of the Lord give joy to the heart. — B96
The queen stands at your right hand, arrayed in gold. — B114
The son of David will live for ever. — B106
The stone rejected by the builders has become the cornerstone. — B60
The waters of the river gladden the city of God, the holy dwelling of the Most
    High. — B117
The Word of God became man and lived among us. — B13
Their message goes out through all the earth. — B110
This is the day the Lord has made; let us rejoice and be glad. — B53, B137
To you, O Lord, I lift my soul. — B129
Today is born our Savior, Christ the Lord. — B7
We are his people: the sheep of his flock. — B145
Who is the king of glory? It is the Lord! — B105
With the Lord there is mercy, and fullness of redemption. — B25, B80, B134
You are my inheritance, O Lord. — B43, B103
You are the honor of our race. — B119
You will draw water joyfully from the springs of salvation. — B16, B46, B71
Your ways, O Lord, are love and truth to those who keep your covenant. — B18